CARNEGIE LEARNING MATH SERIES COURSE 1

STUDENT ASSIGNMENTS

Carnegie Learning >

Carnegie Learning >

437 Grant St., Suite 2000
Pittsburgh, PA 15219
Phone 412.690.2442
Customer Service Phone 877.401.2527
Fax 412.690.2444

www.carnegielearning.com

Acknowledgments

We would like to thank those listed here who helped prepare the *Carnegie Learning Math Series*.

Core Authors
- William S. Hadley, Algebra and Proportional Reasoning
- Mary Lou Metz, Data Analysis and Probability
- Mary Lynn Raith, Number and Operations
- Janet Sinopoli, Algebra
- Jaclyn Snyder, Geometry and Measurement

Contributing Authors
- Janet Falkowski
- Ken Labuskes
- Marianne O'Connor
- Jennifer Panasko
- Agnes Pavolovich

Carnegie Learning Curriculum Development Team
- Sandy Bartle, Senior Academic Officer
- David Dengler, Director, Curriculum Development
- Joshua Fisher, Math Editor
- Jen Gansberger, Editorial Assistant
- David "Augie" Rivera, Math Editor
- Lezlee Ross, Curriculum Developer

Advisory Board
- Shelly Allen, Richmond County Schools
- Ryan Baker, Worcester Polytechnic Institute
- Bill Bush, University of Louisville
- John McCook, McCook and Associates
- Roxana Moreno, University of New Mexico
- Doug Rohrer, University of South Florida
- Bob Siegler, Carnegie Mellon University
- Mary Ann Stine, Private Consultant

Vendors
- Bookmasters, Inc.
- ESI Design
- Mathematical Expressions
- Nesbitt Graphics, Inc.
- Hess Print Solutions

Special Thanks
- Peter Arkle for the design and rendering of "The Crew."
- Richmond County School District, Georgia, for piloting lessons and providing implementation feedback.
- Carnegie Learning Managers of School Partnership for content and design review.
- The Children of Carnegie Learning employees for providing a "middle-schooler's" perspective, with special recognition to:
  Matthew B.
  Dawson D.
  Allison M.
  Adam, Nic, and Shane R.
  Aaron and Melinda R.

ISBN: 978-1-60972-113-8
Student Assignments, Course 1

Printed in the United States of America
2-05/2013 B&B

Lesson 1.1 Assignment

NAME_____ DATE _____

Collection Connections
Factors and Multiples

1. Hector is an event coordinator for a hotel. One of his jobs is to design seating arrangements for groups who reserve meeting rooms. He needs to set up an array of chairs for 60 people.

   a. Determine the distinct factors of 60.

   b. List the factor pairs of 60.

   c. How does listing the factor pairs help Hector with his task?

   d. Hector decides that the chairs best fit in the meeting room using 3 rows of 20 chairs. What does this tell you about the shape of the meeting room?

1

2. Tamara needs to set up an array of chairs in a room for 60 people. The room is in the shape of a square.

   a. Can Tamara arrange all 60 chairs in a square array? Explain your reasoning.

   b. Using the factor pairs, how should Tamara arrange all 60 chairs to come as close to a square as possible? Use a complete sentence in your answer.

3. Jorge needs to set up as many hotel meeting rooms as he can with exactly 60 chairs each. The hotel has a total of 700 meeting chairs. Will he use all of the chairs? Explain your answer.

Lesson 1.2   Assignment

NAME_____ DATE _____

Models and More
Physical Models of Factors and Multiples

1. Mr. McNeal is the director of a university's 120-member marching band. Part of his job is to develop the field formations for the band's half-time performance. He wants the band to begin the performance in the shape of a rectangle.

   a. Draw all of the possible distinct area models to represent the rectangles Mr. McNeal has to choose from using grid paper. Label the dimensions.

   b. List the distinct factors of 120.

2. Ms. Teague is the director of a university's 120-member marching band. The band is joined by 30 dancers for all home games. This means her starting formation must sometimes include 150 people. Her goal is to have the same number of rows in the starting formation for both away and home games.

   a. Draw all of the possible distinct area models to represent the rectangles Ms. Teague has to choose from for home games using grid paper. Label the dimensions.

   b. List the distinct factors of 150.

1

c. Complete the Venn diagram for the factors of 120 and 150.

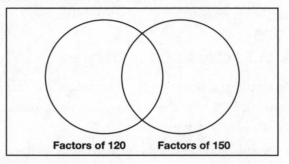

Factors of 120   Factors of 150

d. What are the common factors of 120 and 150?

e. What do the common factors of 120 and 150 represent? Use a complete sentence in your answer.

f. How many rows do you think Ms. Teague should use for her starting formation? Explain your answer.

NAME_____ DATE _____

Sifting for Prime Numbers
Investigating Prime and Composite Numbers

Determine if the number is prime or composite. If it is composite, name a factor other than 1 and the number itself.

1. 35

2. 41

3. 91

4. 86

5. 39

6. 2

7. Complete the maze by coloring squares to follow a path of prime numbers. The path does not use diagonals.

START

3	97	28	27	813	159	427	979	320	219	357	649	573	119	889	407
21	53	15	207	838	87	704	757	907	23	335	482	948	825	236	801
85	127	263	541	17	103	969	607	875	773	451	317	149	797	37	89
72	226	589	554	999	347	79	211	435	983	33	11	393	221	129	463
39	701	181	199	123	86	369	130	93	827	159	113	679	995	792	557
87	733	284	29	681	51	777	866	984	433	105	233	59	566	885	101
50	241	688	283	593	373	71	449	947	661	381	710	677	253	209	13
9	503	507	567	111	622	309	699	161	92	501	44	997	391	718	47
15	919	77	387	903	724	615	95	441	117	741	339	271	973	401	151
63	61	753	938	359	173	419	171	767	598	203	525	523	45	631	721
57	89	421	569	859	993	881	277	109	83	311	857	487	153	67	19

NAME_____ DATE _____

Divisibility Rules!
Investigating Divisibility Rules

Write a number that matches the description using the divisibility rules.

1. three-digit number divisible by 9 and 10

2. four-digit number divisible by 8 and 9

3. four-digit number divisible by 3 and 8

4. four-digit number divisible by 4 and 5

5. four-digit number divisible by 6 and 10

6. five-digit number divisible by 4 and 6

1

7. Ronna volunteers at a food bank. Her job is to distribute the food among the local food pantries served by the bank. The bank's food supply consists of 472 jars of peanut butter, 1620 cans of soup, 1296 jars of sauce, and 1440 boxes of pasta.

   a. Can Ronna evenly distribute the food between 9 food pantries and use all of the food? Show your work for each food item and explain your answer.

   b. At the last minute, Ronna receives word that one of the food pantries is not able to operate due to an emergency. She must now redistribute the food. Can she evenly distribute the food between 8 food pantries and use all of the food? Show your work for each food item and explain your answer.

NAME_____ DATE _____

8. A local food pantry receives its monthly delivery of 59 jars of peanut butter, 202 cans of soup, 162 jars of sauce, and 180 boxes of pasta. This food pantry operates twice each month.

   a. Can the food shipment be evenly divided by 2? Explain your answer.

   b. How much of each type of food is set aside for each of the two distribution days? Explain your answer.

1

   c. On one of the distribution days, the food pantry provides food to 15 families. Are they able to evenly divide any of the types of food by 15? Explain your answer.

9. Write a divisibility rule for 15. (Hint: It is similar to the divisibility rule for 6.)

Lesson 2.1 Assignment

NAME_____ DATE _____

The Think Tank
Prime Factorization and Factor Trees

Rewrite each expression using the indicated properties. Show your work.

1. $4 \times (7 \times 9)$ using the Commutative Property of Multiplication and then applying the Associative Property of Multiplication.

2. $5 \times (6 \times 4)$ using the Associative Property of Multiplication and then applying the Commutative Property of Multiplication.

Determine the prime factorization of each number using a factor tree. Then write the prime factorization using powers.

3. 49

4. 175

5. 88

6. 108

7. 2025

8. Name a number that has a prime factorization with 3 distinct factors.

Lesson 2.2   Assignment

NAME_____ DATE _____

Together Again
Investigating Multiples and Least Common Multiples

1. Ronna is a quality control engineer in a car parts factory. Part of her job is to make sure the parts are the right size.

   a. In one section of the factory, two machines mold different parts that will eventually be put together in an assembly plant. The first machine makes a part every 12 seconds, and the second machine makes a part every 45 seconds. Ronna decides to test these parts each time they both come out of the machines at the same time. How often does Ronna test the parts? Show your work and express your answer in minutes.

   b. Nearby, three machines mold different parts that will be put together. The first machine makes a part every 8 seconds, the second machine makes a part every 15 seconds, and the third machine makes a part every 32 seconds. Ronna tests these three parts each time they all come out of the machines at the same time. How often does Ronna test the parts? Show your work and express your answer in minutes.

2

c. How often will Ronna have to test both sets of parts at the same time? Show your work and express your answer in minutes.

d. Ronna cannot test both sets of parts at the same time. Which set of parts do you think she should check when the sets coincide? Explain your reasoning.

NAME_____ DATE _____

Happenings at Harvest Day
Investigating Factors and Greatest Common Factors

1. Mr. Ellis runs an after-school program for nine- and ten-year-olds. Each day the children participate in an activity or sport and receive a snack. One afternoon, 56 nine-year-olds and 42 ten-year-olds attend the after-school program.

   a. Mr. Ellis wants to make basketball teams that have an equal number of nine- and ten-year-olds. How many different teams can be made? Show your work.

   b. What is the greatest number of teams Mr. Ellis can make so each team has an equal number?

   c. Do you think Mr. Ellis should make the greatest number of teams he can? Explain your reasoning.

2

d. There are 28 nine-year-old girls and 27 ten-year-old girls. Can Mr. Ellis make teams with an equal number of nine- and ten-year-olds and an equal number of each aged girl? Show your work.

2. The children in Mr. Ellis's class assemble care packages for people serving in the military. Mr. Ellis has 30 decks of cards, 150 sets of stationery, and 75 crossword puzzle books. What is the greatest number of care packages that the children can make if they want to use all of the items and have the same number of each item in each care package? Show your work.

3. Do you prefer to calculate the GCF of two numbers by listing factors or by determining the prime factorization? Explain your reasoning.

Lesson 2.4   Assignment

NAME_____ DATE _____

Common Factors or Common Multiples?
Using GCF and LCM to Solve Problems

1. How do you know whether to use common factors or common multiples to solve a problem?

2. Mr. Trocki is the groundskeeper for a vacation resort. He has programmed the sprinkler system to run at night in three different zones. The sprinklers turn on at midnight and run until 7:00 AM. The first zone turns on every 90 minutes, the second zone turns on every 40 minutes, and the third zone turns on every 45 minutes.

   a. List the times the sprinklers will turn on in each zone.

   b. How many times after midnight will all three zones turn on at the same time? At what time(s) will this happen?

2

c. How many minutes after midnight will all three zones turn on at the same time? Explain. Show your work.

d. Mr. Trocki has learned that the resort's guests have complained early in the morning about low water pressure when all three sprinkler zones are going at once. What can he do to solve this problem?

e. Write a word problem within the context of the vacation resort that can be solved by determining the greatest common factor.

Lesson 3.1 Assignment

NAME_____ DATE _____

Flags and Fractions
Modeling Parts of a Whole

1. Use an example to show the difference between a whole object and a set. Then explain the difference in your own words.

2. The mosaic panel shown includes 60 individual hexagonal tiles. The centers of the flowers are yellow and the petals are blue. The rest of the tiles form the white background.

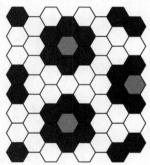

   a. What fraction of the mosaic panel is yellow?

   b. What fraction of the mosaic panel is blue?

   c. What fraction of the mosaic panel is white?

3. A local home design store allows you to design your own mosaic panels. Each panel includes 60 hexagonal tiles. You want to try some of your own designs using only blue and white. The store recommends creating designs that divide the panel into halves, thirds, fourths, fifths, or sixths.

a. Shade a design that represents $\frac{1}{2}$ of the panel.

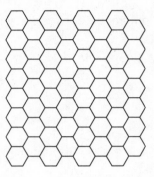

b. Shade a design that represents $\frac{3}{4}$ of the panel.

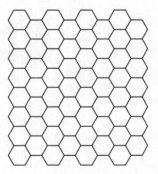

NAME_____ DATE_____

c. Shade a design that represents $\frac{2}{5}$ of the panel.

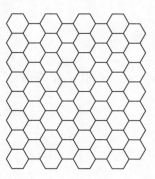

d. Shade a design that represents $\frac{1}{6}$ of the panel.

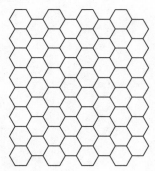

e. Why do you think the store might have chosen to make its panels include 60 tiles?

f. Each color comes in a package of 20 tiles. Explain why a design that uses thirds is the most economical.

3

NAME_____ DATE _____

You Mean Three Can Be One?
Fractional Representations

Pattern blocks have been used to make the shape of a duck. The entire duck represents one whole.

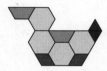

1. Determine what fractional part of the duck each pattern block shape represents.
Explain your reasoning.

a. 1 hexagon

b. 1 trapezoid

c. 1 rhombus

d. 1 triangle

2. Determine what fractional part of the duck shown each group of pattern block shapes represents. Explain your reasoning.

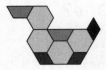

a. Hexagons

b. Trapezoids

c. Rhombi

d. Triangles

NAME_____ DATE _____

3. Determine what fractional part of the duck shown each body part represents. Explain your reasoning.

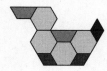

   a. Beak

   b. Head (including the beak)

   c. Body (including the tail)

   d. Shade $\frac{1}{2}$ of the duck.

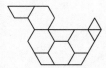

Lesson 3.3 Assignment

NAME_____ DATE _____

Rocket Strips
Dividing a Whole into Fractional Parts

Label the number line to represent the fractional part provided. Then plot each fraction.

1. tenths

a. $\frac{1}{10}$

b. $\frac{4}{10}$

c. $\frac{9}{10}$

d. $\frac{7}{10}$

0   1

2. sixths

a. $\frac{2}{6}$

b. $\frac{3}{6}$

c. $\frac{4}{6}$

d. $\frac{6}{6}$

0   1

3. eighths

a. $\frac{0}{8}$

b. $\frac{1}{8}$

c. $\frac{5}{8}$

d. $\frac{6}{8}$

0   1

Divide the strips into equal parts and shade to show that the given fractions are equivalent.

4. Show that $\frac{3}{4}$ is equivalent to $\frac{6}{8}$.

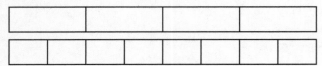

5. Show that $\frac{1}{4}$ is equivalent to $\frac{3}{12}$.

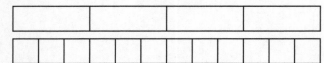

Divide the strips into equal parts and shade to determine the equivalent fraction.

6. How many 12ths are equivalent to $\frac{3}{4}$?

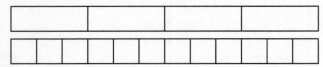

7. How many 10ths are equivalent to $\frac{1}{5}$?

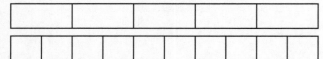

Lesson 3.4 Assignment

NAME_____ **DATE** _____

Getting Closer
Benchmark Fractions

Fill in the missing numerator or denominator so the fraction is close to, but greater than $\frac{1}{2}$.

1. $\dfrac{}{15}$

2. $\dfrac{}{11}$

3. $\dfrac{7}{}$

4. $\dfrac{19}{}$

5. $\dfrac{}{14}$

6. $\dfrac{}{20}$

Fill in the missing numerator or denominator so the fraction is close to, but less than 1.

7. $\dfrac{}{9}$

8. $\dfrac{9}{}$

9. $\dfrac{4}{}$

10. $\dfrac{}{8}$

11. $\dfrac{12}{}$

12. $\dfrac{}{13}$

13. Kara walks five days each week. This week she walked $\frac{7}{8}$ mile on Monday, $\frac{3}{5}$ mile on Tuesday, $\frac{4}{10}$ mile on Wednesday, $\frac{1}{10}$ mile on Thursday, and $\frac{9}{10}$ mile on Friday. Use benchmark fractions to estimate the total distance Kara walked this week. Explain your reasoning.

14. The table shows the fraction of an hour that each student spent running laps at track practice one afternoon.

Student	Fraction of One Hour Spent Running Laps
Denise	$\frac{1}{10}$
Patrick	$\frac{2}{3}$
Tyrone	$\frac{11}{12}$
Su Lee	$\frac{3}{4}$
Jasmine	$\frac{7}{15}$

a. What benchmark fraction should Coach Arnold use to help her determine which students ran laps for more than and which ran laps for less than 30 minutes? Explain your reasoning.

b. Which students ran laps for less than 30 minutes? Explain your reasoning.

c. Which students ran laps for more than 30 minutes? Explain your reasoning.

d. Did any of the students run laps for almost an hour? Explain your reasoning.

15. Use benchmark fractions to order the fractions $\frac{3}{7}$, $\frac{4}{5}$, $\frac{5}{9}$, and $\frac{1}{8}$ from least to greatest. Explain your reasoning.

NAME_____ DATE _____

16. A school participates in a reading contest. The table shows each sixth grade class' portion of the grade's total reading minutes. Use benchmark fractions to help you order the classes from the greatest number of reading minutes to the least. Explain your reasoning.

Class	Portion of Reading Minutes
Mr. Karlie	$\frac{5}{12}$
Ms. Jacobs	$\frac{1}{18}$
Ms. Suarez	$\frac{4}{9}$
Mr. Mitchell	$\frac{1}{12}$

17. What fractions between 0 and 1 other than $\frac{1}{2}$ might be useful benchmark fractions? Explain.

Lesson 3.5 Assignment

NAME_____ DATE _____

What's My Cut?
Equivalent Fractions

1. Each year your school puts on a show to showcase student talent. This year the talent show includes 36 acts as shown in the table.

Type of Act	Number of Acts	Portion of Show	GCF	Simplified Portion of Show
Singing	10			
Dancing	9			
Playing an instrument	8			
Lip-synching	4			
Other	5			

   a. What portion of the show is each type of act? Complete the third column of the table with a fraction that has a denominator of 36.

   b. Complete the fourth column of the table with the GCF of the numerator and denominator of the fraction in the third column.

   c. Complete the last column of the table with the simplified portion of the show for each type of act.

2. Explain how being able to write equivalent fractions can help you to order fractions. Use complete sentences in your answer.

3. Use equivalent fractions to list the fractions $\frac{3}{8}$, $\frac{2}{3}$, $\frac{4}{9}$, $\frac{7}{12}$, $\frac{1}{2}$, and $\frac{5}{24}$ in descending order. Show your work.

NAME_____ DATE _____

Trail Mix
Adding and Subtracting Fractions with Like and Unlike Denominators

1. Raul plays the trumpet in his school's band. He tries to practice at least four days each week. The table shows his practice time for the week.

Day	Practice Time (hours)
Monday	$\frac{1}{12}$
Tuesday	$\frac{1}{6}$
Wednesday	$\frac{1}{4}$
Thursday	$\frac{1}{3}$

a. How long did Raul practice his trumpet on Monday and Tuesday? Show your work.

b. How long did Raul practice his trumpet on Wednesday and Thursday? Show your work.

c. Raul's music teacher recommends that he practice his trumpet at least one hour each week. As of Thursday, has Raul practiced his trumpet at least one hour? Show your work.

d. How much longer does Raul have to practice on Friday if he wants to follow his teacher's recommendation exactly? Show your work.

e. Raul practiced his trumpet for $\frac{5}{12}$ hour on Friday. How much longer did he practice than he needed to? Show your work.

Lesson 3.7   Assignment

NAME_____ DATE _____

Trail Mix Extravaganza
Improper Fractions and Mixed Numbers

Write each mixed number as an improper fraction.

1. $3\frac{1}{5}$

2. $2\frac{3}{7}$

3. $5\frac{8}{9}$

Write each improper fraction as a mixed number.

4. $\frac{7}{3}$

5. $\frac{23}{6}$

6. $\frac{81}{20}$

7. Kiana's pediatrician measures her height at each yearly checkup. The table shows her height at different ages.

Age (years)	Height (feet)
1	$2\frac{1}{2}$
2	$2\frac{11}{12}$
3	
4	$3\frac{3}{4}$

   a. How much did Kiana grow from age 1 to 2? Show your work.

b. Kiana grew $\frac{1}{2}$ foot from age 2 to 3 but the doctor did not fill in the chart. What was her height at age 3? Complete the table. Show your work.

c. How much did Kiana grow from age 3 to 4? Show your work.

d. Use addition to determine how much Kiana grew from age 1 to 4. Show your work.

e. Use subtraction to verify your answer. Show your work.

Lesson 3.8 Assignment

Pizzas by the Slice—or the Rectangle!
Parts of Parts

1. A triathlon competition consists of swimming, cycling, and running. Not all races cover the same distances. According to USA Triathlon, the international distance triathlon consists of $\frac{9}{10}$ mile swimming, $24\frac{4}{5}$ miles cycling, and $6\frac{1}{5}$ miles running. One of the most famous triathlons is an Ironman competition. Competitors in an Ironman competition must swim $2\frac{2}{3}$ times farther than competitors in an international distance triathlon.

   a. Use benchmark fractions to estimate how far competitors must swim in an Ironman triathlon. Show your work.

   b. Calculate the exact distance competitors in an Ironman triathlon must swim. Show your work.

c. Competitors in an Ironman competition must bike $4\frac{16}{31}$ times farther than competitors in an international distance triathlon. Use benchmark fractions to estimate how far competitors must bike in an Ironman triathlon. Show your work.

d. Calculate the exact distance competitors in an Ironman triathlon must bike. Show your work.

e. Competitors in an Ironman competition must run $4\frac{7}{31}$ times farther than competitors in an international distance triathlon. Use benchmark fractions to estimate how far competitors must run in an Ironman triathlon. Show your work.

f. Calculate the exact distance competitors in an Ironman triathlon must run. Show your work.

3

Lesson 3.9   Assignment

NAME_____ DATE _____

Yours Is to Reason Why!
Parts in a Part

1. Ling is a camp counselor at a local summer camp. She is in charge of the weekly craft activity for 40 campers. She plans to make fabric-covered frames that each require $\frac{1}{6}$ yard of fabric. The camp director gave her $6\frac{2}{3}$ yards of fabric remnants for this project.

   a. Based on the information given, does Ling have enough fabric for her craft activity? Show your work.

   b. When Ling actually sets up for her craft activity, she realizes that the director gave her four separate fabric remnants. The table shows how much of each fabric she has. How many campers can use plaid fabric? Show your work.

Fabric	Amount (yards)
Plaid	$\frac{11}{12}$
Tie-dyed	$1\frac{7}{9}$
Striped	$2\frac{2}{9}$
Polka-dotted	$1\frac{3}{4}$

c. How many campers can use tie-dyed fabric? Show your work.

d. How many campers can use the striped fabric? Show your work.

NAME_____ DATE _____

e. How many campers can use the polka-dotted fabric? Show your work.

f. After considering the four individual fabric remnants, does Ling have enough fabric for her craft activity? Explain your answer.

3

NAME_____ DATE _____

Divide Your Time Well, and Your Trail Mix, and Your . . .
Mixed Number Division

1. Elena wants to make a mix CD of some of her favorite songs. The CD has 60 minutes of available space.

   a. Elena wonders how many songs she will be able to include on her CD. She looks online and finds a source that says the average song length is $3\frac{1}{2}$ minutes. If this is true, how many songs will Elena be able to include on the CD? Show your work.

   b. Elena looks at the list of songs that she would like to include on her CD and notices that, on average, her favorite songs have a length of $4\frac{2}{5}$ minutes. How many $4\frac{2}{5}$ -minute songs can Elena include on her CD? Show your work.

c. Ms. Hendrix, Elena's mom, tells her that when she was a girl, she used to make mix cassette tapes with her favorite songs. One side of Ms. Hendrix's cassette tapes had $22\frac{1}{2}$ minutes of available space. How many $4\frac{2}{5}$ -minute songs could Ms. Hendrix record on one side of a cassette tape? Show your work.

d. Use estimation to help explain how you know that your answer to part (c) is reasonable.

2. Ms. Hendrix thinks that the average length of a song is 3 minutes. If this is true, how many 3-minute songs could be recorded on one side of a cassette tape if each side has $22\frac{1}{2}$ minutes of available space? Show your work.

NAME_____ DATE _____

3. If Ms. Hendrix would like to record 6 songs on one side of a cassette tape, what is the maximum length the songs could be if each side has $22\frac{1}{2}$ minutes of available space? Show your work.

Lesson 4.1 Assignment

NAME_____ DATE _____

Minty Fresh–Coins?
Introduction to Decimals

1. Your hometown is known for getting a lot of snowfall in the winter. Your science teacher asks you to research the five snowiest days in your town's history and to do a presentation of your findings for the class. The table shows the results of your research.

Date	Snowfall (feet)
January 10, 1923	2.75
March 9, 1933	3.325
December 17, 1964	1.8
January 26, 1987	2.33
February 12, 2001	3.08

a. You want to create a number line illustration to go along with your presentation. Plot and label the snowfalls from the table on the number line given.

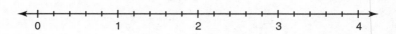

b. During your presentation you will have to read the decimal snowfall amounts aloud to the class. To make sure that you read the decimals correctly, you write them out on index cards ahead of time. Write each snowfall amount from the table in words.

4

Lesson 4.2 Assignment

You Be the Judge
Comparing, Ordering, Estimating, and Rounding Decimals

1. You are trying to order a list of decimals that have the same whole number portion to the left of the decimal point. Explain why it is helpful to rewrite each decimal to have the same number of decimal places.

2. Jeremy's dog had four puppies. He could not bring himself to give any of the puppies away, so he kept them all! The chart shows their birth weights and adult weights.

Puppy	Birth Weight (pounds)	Adult Weight (pounds)
Mo	0.75	21.875
Lava	1.1875	21.6
Jake	0.725	21.92
Cammie	1.2	18.025

a. Explain why you can quickly determine which two puppies were the smallest at birth and which two puppies were the largest at birth.

b. Compare the two smallest puppies at birth. Show your work and explain your reasoning.

c. Compare the two largest puppies at birth. Show your work and explain your reasoning.

d. List the puppies from smallest to largest at birth. Show your work and explain your reasoning.

e. Round the adult weights of the dogs to the nearest one, to the nearest tenth, and to the nearest hundredth. Explain your answers.

NAME_____ DATE _____

f. Which rounding helps you to order the weights from largest to smallest? Explain.

g. List the dogs from largest to smallest based on their adult weights.

4

Lesson 4.3 Assignment

NAME_____ DATE _____

The Ancient Spaniards Didn't Count the Thumbs!
Fraction-Decimal Equivalents

Write each fraction as a decimal. Rewrite the denominator as a power of 10, if necessary.

1. $\dfrac{33}{100}$

2. $\dfrac{627}{10,000}$

3. $\dfrac{149}{250}$

4. $\dfrac{27}{40}$

5. $\dfrac{72}{200}$

6. $\dfrac{2012}{4000}$

7. Explain when you might choose to write a fraction as a decimal by rewriting the denominator as a power of 10. Use complete sentences in your answer.

Write each fraction as a decimal. If necessary, round to the nearest hundredth or use bar notation to show a repeating decimal.

8. $\frac{15}{19}$

9. $\frac{5}{9}$

10. $\frac{23}{54}$

11. $\frac{87}{642}$

NAME_____ DATE _____

12. $\dfrac{3}{423}$

13. $\dfrac{499}{502}$

14. $\dfrac{25}{99}$

15. $\dfrac{246}{1999}$

4

16. $\dfrac{1264}{8653}$

4

17. A middle school has 549 students. Twenty-seven of the students have summer birthdays. Write the fraction of students with summer birthdays as a decimal. Round the decimal to the nearest hundredth.

Lesson 4.4   Assignment

NAME_____ DATE _____

When Less Is Better
Adding and Subtracting Decimals

1. Explain how estimating the sum or difference of decimals before performing the actual calculation is helpful.

2. Kendra is a huge fan of Broadway musicals. She wants to burn a CD of some of her favorite shows. The table shows the musicals she has chosen and how much space they each take up in megabytes.

Musicals	Disc Space (megabytes)
Annie	109.785
Beauty and the Beast	131.642
Into the Woods	79.4
Les Miserables	192.27
Shrek – The Musical	117.005

a. Estimate the total amount of space the musicals will take up on the CD. Show your work.

b. Calculate the total amount of space the musicals will take up on the CD. Show your work.

c. If a CD can hold 700 megabytes, how much space will Kendra still have on the CD? First estimate, then calculate the answer. Show your work.

d. The musical *The Secret Garden* takes up 88.53 megabytes of space. Can Kendra fit this musical on the CD? If not, by how many megabytes is she over? Show your work.

NAME_____ **DATE** _____

e. Kendra decides she really wants to have the musical *Wicked* on the CD. *Wicked* takes up 129.907 megabytes of space. If she leaves *Into the Woods* off of the CD, will she have enough space for *Wicked*? Explain.

4

NAME_____ DATE _____

I Just Spent One Week Going to Work!
Multiplying Decimals

1. Explain how estimating the product of decimals before performing the actual calculation is helpful.

2. When you multiply a decimal greater than zero by a decimal greater than one, what do you know about the product compared to the first decimal? Use a complete sentence in your answer.

3. When you multiply a decimal greater than zero by a decimal between zero and one, what do you know about the product compared to the first decimal? Use a complete sentence in your answer.

4. There are many trends in society that affect what Americans do. The current focus on being fit and healthy has made a difference in what Americans drink.

   a. In 1980, the average American's whole-milk consumption was 6.3 times that of his or her bottled water consumption. Estimate how many gallons of whole milk each American drank in 1980, and then calculate the actual answer. Write the answer, rounded to the nearest tenth, in the table. Show your work.

Year	Bottled Water (gallons)	Whole Milk (gallons)
1980	2.7	
1990	8.8	
2000	16.7	
2007		

   b. In 1990, the average American's whole-milk consumption was 1.19 times that of his or her bottled-water consumption. Estimate how many gallons of whole milk each American drank in 1990, and then calculate the actual answer. Write the answer, rounded to the nearest tenth, in the table. Show your work.

NAME_____ **DATE** _____

c. In 2000, the average American's whole-milk consumption was 0.485 times that of his or her bottled-water consumption. Estimate how many gallons of whole milk each American drank in 2000, and then calculate the actual answer. Write the answer, rounded to the nearest tenth, in the table. Show your work.

d. In 2007, the average American drank 1.74 times the amount of bottled water he or she drank in 2000. Using the data from the table, estimate how many gallons of bottled water each American drank in 2007, and then calculate the actual answer. Write the answer, rounded to the nearest tenth, in the table. Show your work.

e. In 2007, the average American's whole-milk consumption was 0.22 times that of his or her bottled-water consumption. Using the data from the table, calculate how many gallons of whole milk each American drank in 2007. Write the answer, rounded to the nearest tenth, in the table. Show your work.

f. If you had to predict the average American's consumption of bottled water for five years beyond 2010, do you think it will continue to increase? Explain your answer.

Lesson 4.6   Assignment

NAME_____ DATE _____

Organized Estimation
Long Division of Whole Numbers

1. Lacrosse is a fast growing sport in the United States. Many communities are starting up youth programs for both boys and girls as young as 3rd grade. The Amber Hills Community has had a youth program for several years, and they rely heavily on fundraisers in order to keep the costs down for all the team members.

   a. Recently, one of the officers of the club was able to get a donation of 6050 candy bars that the athletes could then sell and keep all the proceeds. If there are 242 athletes in the club, how many candy bars must each athlete sell? Will there be any candy bars left over?

   b. Some of the money that they raise will be used to buy new balls. They buy a total of 330 balls. If there are 22 teams in the organization, how many balls will each team get? Will there be any balls left over?

c. After a discount, the price of the jerseys came to $6776. How much will each athlete have to pay for their jersey?

d. The organization also makes money by running a concession stand for each of their home games. The local supermarket donated 45 packs of hot dogs that have 12 hot dogs in each pack. Packages of hot dog buns need to be purchased. If there are 8 buns in each bag, how many bags should be bought? Will there be any extra buns? If so, how many?

NAME_____ **DATE** _____

e. The club also holds one weekend tournament each year as part of their fundraising efforts. This year they have decided to hand out gift bags to each athlete. One local bank donated 3000 pens. If there are 335 total athletes entered in the tournament, how many pens should they put in each bag? Will there be any extra pens? If so, how many?

f. At the end of the season, the organization gives out $25 gift cards to each of their head coaches. They ask the parents to donate to this fund. They have collected a total of $530. Do they have enough money for all of the coaches? If not, how much more do they need?

4

Lesson 4.7 Assignment

NAME_____ DATE _____

Los Angeles Commute Didn't Top the List?
Dividing Decimals

Write a division problem that has the same quotient as the division expression given.

1. $36.5 \div 0.005$

2. $63.196 \div 14.8$

3. $440.618 \div 3.02$

4. Nina just bought a new car and wanted to verify the advertised gas mileage of 21 miles per gallon in the city and 27 miles per gallon on the highway. She received the car with a full tank of gas. The table shows how far she drove and how much gas she had to put in to fill up the gas tank.

Fill-Up	Distance Driven (miles)	Amount of Gas (gallons)	Gas Mileage (mi/gal)
1	316.2	12.8	
2	313.7	13.125	
3	375.4	14.327	
4	236.9	10.95	

a. Estimate Nina's gas mileage for her first fill-up, and then calculate the actual answer. Write the answer, rounded to the nearest tenth, in the table. Show your work.

b. Estimate Nina's gas mileage for her second fill-up, and then calculate the actual answer. Write the answer, rounded to the nearest tenth, in the table. Show your work.

NAME_____ DATE _____

c. Estimate Nina's gas mileage for her third fill-up, and then calculate the actual answer. Write the answer, rounded to the nearest tenth, in the table. Show your work.

d. Estimate Nina's gas mileage for her fourth fill-up, and then calculate the actual answer. Write the answer, rounded to the nearest tenth, in the table. Show your work.

e. What is the average gas mileage for Nina's first four fill-ups? Show your work.

f. Nina checked her gas mileage in the spring when she got the new car. Now that it is winter, she wants to check her mileage again. She traveled 282 miles on 14.25 gallons of gas. Calculate her gas mileage to the nearest tenth. Show your work.

Lesson 5.1 Assignment

NAME_____ DATE _____

Mixing Paint
Introduction to Ratios

The Lewis brothers just joined MovieQ, a club that sends movies to their house based on a list that they pre-select. The boys work together to pick the first 10 movies for their list, each brother adding to the list based on their favorite type of movie. John David puts 5 sports movies on the list; Parker chooses 3 war movies; and Stephen adds 2 comedies.

1. Write the ratio that expresses the relationship using a colon and in fractional form. Identify whether it is a part-to-part or part-to-whole ratio.

   a. sports movies to war movies

   b. comedies to total movies

   c. war movies to comedies

   d. sports movies to total movies

    e. comedies to sports movies

    f. war movies to total movies

2. Complete the ratio table.

Total number of movies	10	20		50	
Number of sports movies	5		20		
Number of war movies	3				30
Number of comedies	2	4			

3. Ms. Lewis decides to buy healthy snacks for her sons during their movie-watching. She can buy bags of fruit that contain 1 pear for every 2 apples. Complete the model shown using the ratio given. Then, calculate your answer from your model, and explain your reasoning.

    a. How many apples are in the bag if there are a total of 9 pieces of fruit?

NAME_____ DATE _____

b. How many apples are in the bag if there are a total of 15 pieces of fruit?

c. How many pieces of fruit are there if there are 8 apples in the bag?

5

5

Lesson 5.2   Assignment

NAME_____ DATE _____

What's in a Name?
Ratio Representations

During the spring sports season, boys at Hillbrook Middle School have the opportunity to either play baseball, run outdoor track, or play lacrosse. Of the 75 boys at Hillbrook who play a spring sport, 30 run track, 25 play baseball, and 20 play lacrosse.

1. Write the following ratios for the spring athletes and determine whether a part-to-part or part-to-whole relationship exists.

   a. track runners to baseball players

   b. track runners to total number of male athletes

   c. baseball players to lacrosse players

   d. baseball players to total number of male athletes

2. Of the 75 boys at Hillbrook who play a spring sport, 30 run track, 25 play baseball, and 20 play lacrosse. Determine which is greater and explain your reasoning: the ratio of baseball players to the total number of male athletes or the ratio or track runners to the total number of male athletes.

3. For the spring sports assembly, Ms. Lytle is going to announce the winning record of the baseball team. She has written several correct statements to describe their record. Describe the meaning of each, including any information that is missing.

   a. The team played 20 games and lost 8 of them.

   b. The baseball team's wins outnumbered their losses by a ratio of 3 to 2.

   c. The baseball team won 6 out of 10 of their games.

   d. The baseball team won 4 more games than they lost.

NAME_____ DATE _____

4. Analyze each statement. Determine whether a part : part or a part : whole relationship exists.

    a. Four out of every seven students play a spring sport at Hillbrook Middle School.

    b. There are 5 girls for every 4 boys at Hillbrook Middle School.

    c. There will be 1 teacher for every 15 students at the spring sports assembly.

    d. Of the 35 students who play lacrosse in the spring, 15 are girls.

    e. There are 10 sprinters on the 30 member boys' track team.

Lesson 5.3   Assignment

NAME_____ DATE _____

I'd Like to Solve the Puzzle . . .
Writing Equivalent Ratios

1. In planning for the upcoming regional girls' tennis tournament, Coach McCarter looked at her players' statistics from the previous 2 months.

Sarah	Sophie	Grace	Cecelia
7 matches won 3 matches lost	15 matches won 5 matches lost	12 matches won 6 matches lost	8 matches won 2 matches lost

   a. Write each tennis player's record as a ratio of matches won to total matches played.

   Sarah:

   Sophie:

   Grace:

   Cecelia:

   b. Based on their records, which player should Coach McCarter choose to attend the regional tournament?

   c. Rank the players in order from the best record to the worst record.

2. In tennis, an ace is a legal serve that cannot be returned and is not even touched by the opponent's racket. Cecelia has an excellent serve. Last week, Cecelia hit 7 aces in 2 matches.

a. If she plays 6 matches in the regional tournament, how many aces should she expect? Explain the scaling factor you used to determine the equivalent ratio.

b. If she plays 10 matches in the regional tournament, how many aces should she expect? Explain the scaling factor you used to determine the equivalent ratio.

c. If her opponent in the first match has hit 9 aces in the last 3 matches, how many aces can Cecelia expect her opponent to hit in their match? Explain the scaling factor you used to determine the equivalent ratio.

NAME_____ DATE _____

3. Coach McCarter is mixing the sports drink for her tennis players at a match. Her players will need 24 quarts of sports drink for the first day of the tournament. Coach McCarter has 3 different types of sports drinks to choose from.

a. Electro-Ade calls for 5 scoops for every 2 quarts of water. If she uses this sports drink, how many scoops of powder will she need?

b. Hydrate calls for 7 scoops for every gallon (4 quarts) of water. If she uses this sports drink, how many scoops of powder will she need?

c. More Than Water calls for 3 scoops for every quart of water. If she uses this sports drink, how many scoops of powder will she need?

4. Because it was so hot at a tennis tournament, 2 out of every 3 spectators in attendance bought a bottle of water.

   a. If there are 270 spectators at the tournament, how many bottles of water did they sell?

   b. If they sold 70 bottles of water, how many spectators were in attendance?

   c. If they sold 202 bottles of water, how many spectators were in attendance?

NAME_____ DATE_____

The Most Important Meal of the Day
Modeling Ratios

A mason is a person who builds structures with bricks, stone, cement block, or tile. A mason usually uses mortar to hold the bricks together. A general rule of thumb in masonry is that $2\frac{1}{2}$ bags of mortar are needed for every 100 cement blocks.

1. Complete the double number line to determine the amount of mortar needed for each quantity of blocks.

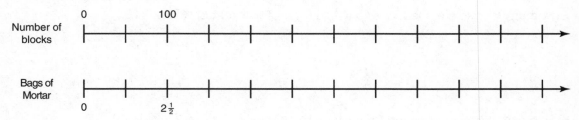

   a. How many bags of mortar will a mason need for 200 blocks?

   b. How many bags of mortar will a mason need for 350 blocks?

   c. How many bags of mortar will a mason need for 50 blocks?

   d. With $12\frac{1}{2}$ bags of mortar, how many blocks can the mason lay?

When building a single layer of a wall, a mason needs 9 cement blocks for every 12 feet of wall.

2. Complete the double number line to determine the number of blocks for each length of wall.

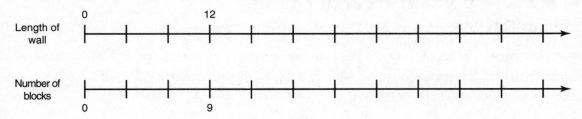

a. How many blocks are needed for a single layer of wall that is 16 feet long?

b. How many blocks are needed for a single layer of wall that is 4 feet long?

c. How many blocks are needed for a single layer of wall that is 36 feet long?

d. If a mason uses 18 blocks to create a single layer of a wall, how long is that wall?

NAME_____ DATE _____

Many masons base the cost for a job on the number of blocks they will need to lay. For example, Doyle Masonry charges $2000 for every 1000 blocks laid.

3. Complete the double number line to determine the charge for each quantity of blocks.

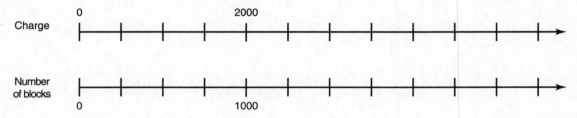

a. What is the charge for laying 250 blocks?

b. What is the charge for laying 1500 blocks?

c. How many blocks were laid if the charge is $5000?

d. How many blocks were laid if the charge is $3500?

Lesson 5.5 Assignment

NAME_____ DATE _____

A Trip to the Moon
Using Tables to Represent Equivalent Ratios

1. In the infant room of the Kids Unlimited daycare, there must be 1 teacher for every 4 infants present. Complete the table to show the number of teachers required given the number of infants. Explain your calculations.

Teachers	1	3					
Infants	4	12	16	28	24	40	64

a. How many teachers are required if there are 8 infants present? Use your table of values and explain your calculations.

b. How many teachers are required if there are 20 infants present? Use your table of values and explain your calculations.

c. How many teachers are required if there are 32 infants present? Use your table of values and explain your calculations.

2. Miss Doris is a teacher in the toddler room at Kids Unlimited daycare. She is buying toys to fill the classroom. She wants to ensure that there are plenty of toys so that the children have lots of options. Complete the table to show the number of toys given the number of children in the toddler room. Explain your reasoning.

Children	3	6		18	
Toys	5		15		45

NAME_____ DATE _____

a. How many toys will Miss Doris buy if there are 15 children in the toddler room? Use your table of values and explain your calculations.

b. How many toys will Miss Doris buy if there are 36 children in the toddler room? Use your table of values and explain your calculations.

3. Miss Jenn is the teacher of a preschool class at Kids Unlimited Daycare. She must split the children's time between playing and learning. For every 30 minutes, the children will spend 18 minutes playing and 12 minutes learning. Complete the table of values.

Total amount of time	30	90		
Playing time	18			144
Learning time	12		48	

a. If the students spent 24 minutes learning, how many minutes did they spend playing? Explain your reasoning.

b. If the students have played for 108 minutes, how many minutes did they spend learning? Explain your reasoning.

c. If the students spent 84 minutes learning, how many minutes did they spend playing? Explain your reasoning.

Graphing Out Equivalence
Using Graphs to Represent Equivalent Ratios

Morgan and her friends are testing their typing skills. Morgan took an online typing test to compare her typing speed with her friends' speeds. During the 2 minute test, she typed 144 words. Her friend, Elizabeth, took a longer test; she typed 150 words in 3 minutes. Their other friend, Ruth, typed 65 words in 1 minute.

1. Complete the tables to show each girl's typing speed.

Morgan						
Time (min)	1	2	3	4	5	6
Words						

Elizabeth						
Time (min)	1	2	3	4	5	6
Words						

Ruth						
Time (min)	1	2	3	4	5	6
Words						

a. Plot each set of equivalent ratios on the graph. Use a × to denote Morgan's typing speed, a □ to denote Elizabeth's typing speed, and a ★ to denote Ruth's typing speed.

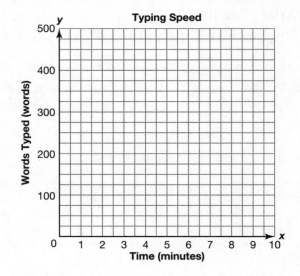

b. Draw three separate lines through the points that represent each ratio. What do you notice?

c. Who is the fastest typist? Who is the slowest typist? Explain how you can tell by looking at the three lines on your graph.

d. Use your graph to estimate how many words Elizabeth can type in 8 minutes.

NAME_____   DATE _____

e. Use your graph to estimate how many words Ruth can type in 7 minutes.

f. Use your graph to estimate how many words Morgan can type in $3\frac{1}{2}$ minutes.

Morgan uses her typing skills to write a research paper for her history class. When she hits "Print," she realizes that her printer is broken—for every 5 pages she attempts to print, the printer messes up 3 of them!

2. Complete the table to display the number of pages her printer would mess up.

Number of pages attempted to print	5	10	15	20
Number of messed up pages				

a. Create a graph for your table of values. Be sure to label the axes and title the graph.

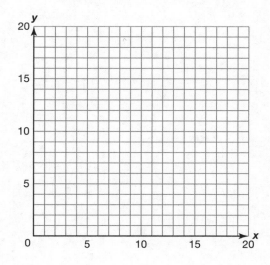

Lesson 5.7   Assignment

NAME_____ **DATE** _____

Water Is a Precious Resource
Using Multiple Ratio Representations to Solve Problems

1. Ellen loves to make her own clothes. With 45 yards of cloth, she can make 5 dresses. Explain your reasoning for each question by using the double number line.

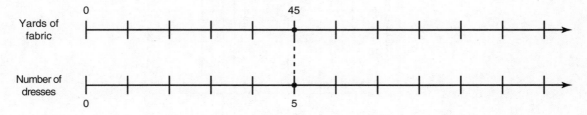

   a. If Ellen has 72 yards of cloth, how many dresses can she make?

   b. If Ellen has 18 yards of cloth, how many dresses can she make?

   c. If Ellen wants to make dresses for her 6 cousins, how many yards of cloth does she need?

   d. If Ellen is going to make a dress for herself, how many yards of cloth does she need?

2. To accessorize her new dresses, Ellen decides to order textured stockings from an online store. The graph shows the costs of orders of stockings.

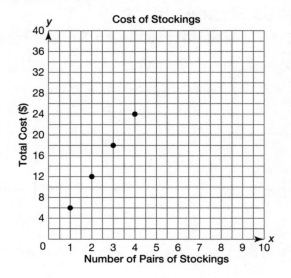

a. Write each point on the graph as a ratio of *number of pairs of stockings : total cost of the order*.

b. How much would an order of 5 pairs of stockings cost? Explain the method you used.

NAME_____ **DATE** _____

    c. How much would an order of 6 pairs of stockings cost? Explain the method you used.

    d. How much would an order of 10 pairs of stockings cost? Explain the method you used.

Lesson 5.8　Assignment

NAME_____　DATE _____

What Is the Better Buy?
Introduction to Unit Rates

1. Damon is buying water bottles for the runners in the upcoming cross country meet. He shops around at 3 different stores to find the best deal on water.

       Store 1: 24 bottles for $6.96

       Store 2: 16 bottles for $4.96

       Store 3: 32 bottles for $10.56

   a. Calculate the price per bottle at each store.

   b. At which store would Damon get the best deal on water?

2. Bananas are a great source of energy for runners before or after a long run. Damon decides to get bunches of bananas for teams of runners to eat at the end of a meet. He gives each team a bunch of bananas to share equally.

       Team 1, which has 5 runners, got a bunch of 6 bananas.

       Team 2, which has 3 runners, got a bunch of 4 bananas.

       Team 3, which has 8 runners, got a bunch of 10 bananas.

   a. How many bananas does each runner on Team 1 get? Explain your work.

   b. How many bananas does each runner on Team 2 get? Explain your work.

c. How many bananas does each runner on Team 3 get? Explain your work.

d. Which team got the most bananas per runner?

3. Beth, Kelly, Andrea, and Amy are all training for the local marathon.

  a. Beth can run 7.5 miles per hour. At this rate, how far will she run in the first 3 hours of the marathon?

  b. Kelly runs 13.5 miles in 2 hours. What is her rate?

  c. Andrea is the slowest runner in the group. She can run 5.5 miles per hour. At this rate, how many miles will she run in the first 3 hours of the marathon?

  d. Amy wants to run the 26 miles of the marathon in 4.5 hours. At what rate will she have to run to reach this goal?

4. At a workout designed to increase speed, Beth runs 800 meters in $2\frac{1}{2}$ minutes. Kelly runs 1600 meters in $4\frac{1}{2}$ minutes. Who is the faster runner in this workout?

Lesson 6.1 Assignment

NAME_____ DATE_____

Percents Can Make or Break You!
Introduction to Percents

Shade each hundredths grid to represent the percent. Then, write the equivalent fraction and decimal.

1. 32%

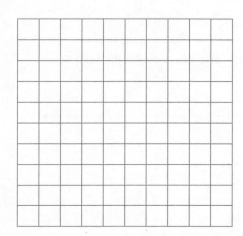

2. 85%

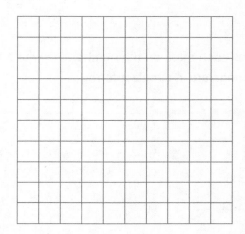

Each hundredths grid represents a whole. Write the shaded part as a fraction, decimal, and percent.

3.

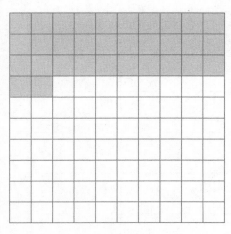

4.

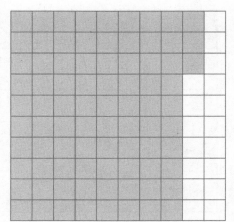

Write each decimal as a percent.

5. 0.61

6. 0.7

7. 0.555

8. Describe how to easily write a decimal as a percent.

9. Label each mark on the number line with a fraction, decimal, and percent. Make sure your fractions are in simplest form.

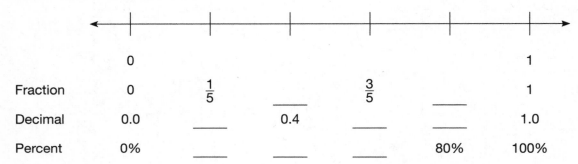

	0				1
Fraction	0	$\frac{1}{5}$	___	$\frac{3}{5}$	___	1
Decimal	0.0	___	0.4	___	___	1.0
Percent	0%	___	___	___	80%	100%

10. The table shows the portions of sixth graders at your school who have each number of siblings. Complete the table by representing each portion as a ratio, a fraction, a decimal, and a percent. Make sure your fractions and ratios are in simplest form.

Number of Siblings	Ratio	Fraction	Decimal	Percent
0		$\frac{3}{20}$		
1				20%
2	3 : 8			
3			0.24	
4 or more		$\frac{7}{200}$		

6

NAME_____ DATE _____

Wacky Weather!
Estimating Percents

1. A community theater is trying to raise money for a new marquee. The shaded region on the sign posted in front of the theater shows the progress so far. Estimate the theater's progress toward its goal as a percent.

2. The students at Penncrest Middle School sold various products for a fall fundraiser. The table shows the percent of profit the school earned and the total amount sold for each type of product.

Product	Percent Profit	Amount Sold
Candy	65%	$6400
Wrapping paper	40%	$1200
Stationery	50%	$900
Calendars	25%	$3120

a. Use benchmark percents to calculate how much profit the school earned on candy. Show your work.

b. Use benchmark percents to calculate how much profit the school made on wrapping paper. Show your work.

c. Use benchmark percents to calculate how much profit the school earned on stationery. Explain your reasoning using complete sentences.

d. Use benchmark percents to calculate how much profit the school earned on calendars. Explain your reasoning using complete sentences.

e. How much total profit did Penncrest Middle School earn during its fall fundraiser? Show your work.

6

f. The school newspaper reported that the students sold $11,620 worth of products and earned the school about 50% profit. Was the newspaper report accurate? Explain.

NAME_____ DATE _____

It's All in the Follow-Through
Determine the Percent of a Number

Mr. Hawkins manages a small store called Action Sporting Goods. He works with percents a lot when planning store sales and calculating sales tax, but he also uses percents for his management duties.

1. Mr. Hawkins wants to make sure that his store is stocked with enough equipment for all of the community sports. He surveys 240 of his customers and asks them to choose the one sport that they're most likely to buy sports equipment for this season.

Sport	Percent of Responses
Basketball	30%
Baseball	20%
Football	35%
Wrestling	15%

   a. How many of his customers will need baseball equipment?

   b. How many of his customers will need wrestling equipment?

   c. How many of his customers will need football equipment?

   d. How many of his customers will need basketball equipment?

2. Mr. Hawkins is going to put his golf equipment on sale at the end of the summer. A set of junior golf clubs at Action Sporting Goods costs $180. Use a double number line to represent the discount available for each percent.

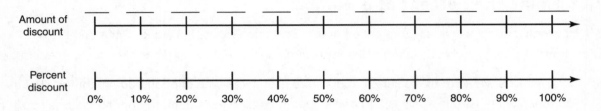

3. Salespeople at Action Sporting Goods get a 20% employee discount on all full-price items they purchase. An employee named Erik buys a football jersey priced at $119.

   a. How much is Erik's discount on the football jersey? Show your work.

   b. How much does Erik have to pay for the football jersey before tax? Show your work.

   c. Explain how to find Erik's discounted price for the football jersey in only one step.

6

NAME_____ DATE _____

4. Action Sporting Goods has a merchant service provider that allows the store to accept credit and debit cards for purchases. This provider charges the store a fee of 3% on all credit and debit sales. Mr. Hawkins double checks the charges from the merchant services provider each month. Last month, the store's credit and debit sales totaled $12,950. What fee should Mr. Hawkins expect to pay the merchant service provider? Show your work.

5. Each month Mr. Hawkins must send a payment for state sales tax. The tax is 6% of the store's taxable sales. The store's taxable sales total for last month was $13,487.

   a. How much is the state sales tax for last month? Show your work.

   b. The state gives a 1% discount on the sales tax due if it is paid on time. How much is the discount? Show your work.

   c. Mr. Hawkins plans to send his sales tax payment in before it is due to receive the 1% discount. How much does Mr. Hawkins have to send for last month's sales tax? Show your work.

Lesson 6.4 Assignment

NAME_____ DATE _____

Mi Mi Mi Mi Mi Mi Mi!
Determine the Part, Whole, or Percent of Percent Problems

Basketball is a popular sport at Union Middle School for both boys and girls.

1. At Union Middle School, 99 boys, or 36% of the boys, play basketball.

   a. How many boys attend Union Middle School? Show your work.

   b. Of the 99 boys who play basketball, 37 are sixth graders. What percent of the boy basketball players are sixth graders? Show your work and round your answer to the nearest percent.

   c. Of the 99 boys who play basketball, 32 are seventh graders. What percent of the boy basketball players are seventh graders? Show your work and round your answer to the nearest percent.

6

d. Of the 99 boys who play basketball, 30 are eighth graders. What percent of the boy basketball players are eighth graders? Show your work and round your answer to the nearest percent.

e. Notice that the number of players and the percents for each grade of boys are the same. Explain why this is the case.

2. At Union Middle School, 55 girls, or 22% of the girls, play basketball.

   a. How many girls attend Union Middle School? Show your work.

   b. Of the 55 girls who play basketball, 25 are sixth graders. What percent of the girl basketball players are sixth graders? Show your work and round your answer to the nearest percent.

Lesson 6.5 Assignment

NAME_____ DATE _____

Practical Percents Practice!
Using Percents in Real-World Situations

Kendall and Kasey haven't seen each other in months! They decide to meet for dinner. During the meal, Kasey tells Kendall all about her new job at The Foot Parade.

1. Kasey tells Kendall about some of the perks of her new job. "We sell the coolest, most stylish shoes, and I get a 35% employee discount on anything I buy!"

   a. How much would Kasey pay for a $75 pair of shoes?

   b. How much would Kasey pay for a $120 pair of boots?

   c. If Kasey got a $5.25 discount on her new flip-flops, how much did they cost originally?

2. "Does The Foot Parade have a lot of shoes to choose from?" Kendall asks Kasey. "We have 675 pairs of shoes in stock!" Kasey replies.

    a. If The Foot Parade has 105 pairs of hiking boots in stock, what percent of their shoe selection is hiking boots? Round your answer to the nearest percent.

    b. If The Foot Parade has 75 pairs of flip-flops in stock, what percent of their shoe selection is flip-flops? Round your answer to the nearest percent.

3. "That sounds like an awesome job!" Kendall replies. "But, is the pay any good?" Kasey explains that she is paid on commission; she earns 17% commission on her sales.

    a. If Kasey sold $550 worth of shoes during her shift yesterday, how much money did she earn?

    b. If Kasey earned $140.25 last Friday, what was the total amount of her sales?

NAME_____ DATE _____

4. "You should come shopping there next weekend," says Kasey. "We're having a great sale—40% off everything."

   a. If Kendall buys a $35 pair of shoes next weekend, how much will she pay after the 6% sales tax?

   b. If Kendall buys a $90 pair of hiking boots next weekend, how much will she pay after the 6% sales tax?

5. After a long dinner together, the waitress arrives with the check. Kasey agrees to pay the $38 bill, and Kendall offers to pay the tip.

   a. What is the total cost, including gratuity, if Kendall wants to give the waitress a 25% tip?

   b. What is the total cost, including gratuity, if Kendall wants to give the waitress a 20% tip?

   c. What is the total cost, including gratuity, if Kendall wants to give the waitress an 18% tip?

6

6

There's a Reason Behind the Rhyme
Order of Operations

1. Darian and his friends formed a band one year ago and are ready to play at local venues. The band earns varying amounts of money for each gig that they play. Several factors affect how much money each member of the band earns for each show, including overhead costs, manager fees, and advertising.

   a. At a recent venue, the band made $500 for the night. They had to subtract the overhead costs of $80 and then divide the remaining money between the band members. If there are 4 members in the band, which numerical expressions correctly shows the amount that each member will make? Explain your answer using the rules for order of operations.

   Expression A   **Expression B**

   $500 - 80 \div 4$ $(500 - 80) \div 4$

b. The band is offered a Friday night spot at a local club for a total of 8 Fridays. The club would like to pay the band the total amount for all 8 Fridays after their last performance. The band decides to advertise their 8 appearances in the local newspaper. The advertising costs are $400. If the band makes $500 for each appearance, which numerical expression correctly shows the amount each member will make? Explain your answer using the rules for order of operations.

Expression A

$(8 \times 500 - 400) \div 4$

Expression B

$8 \times 500 - 400 \div 4$

c. The band finds itself growing in popularity, so they hire a manager. The manager asks a local park if they can hold a concert on one of the lawn areas. The park consents to the concert, but only if the concertgoers sit on folding chairs for the concert. The lawn can have 20 rows of seats with 20 chairs in each row. The band charges $25 for each seat. The overhead for advertising, the rental of the chairs, and the management fees totals $4000. If the band is able to fill all of the seats, which solution shows the amount the band will make? Determine the error that was made in the incorrect solution.

Solution A

$25 \times 20^2 - 4000$

$= 25 \times 400 - 4000$

$= 10,000 - 4000$

$= 6000$

Solution B

$25 \times 20^2 - 4000$

$= 500^2 - 4000$

$= 250,000 - 4000$

$= 246,000$

d. The manager wants to sell T-shirts at the concert with the band's name on them. Based on figures from other bands, the manager decides to make 240 T-shirts to sell. It will cost $6 to have each T-shirt made, but they will sell the T-shirts for $15. They end up selling only half of the T-shirts. Which solution shows the amount the band will make from producing and selling the T-shirts? Determine the error that was made in the incorrect solution.

Solution A

$240 \div 2 \times 15 - 240 \times 6$

$= 240 \div 30 - 240 \times 6$

$= 8 - 1440$

$= -1432$

Solution B

$240 \div 2 \times 15 - 240 \times 6$

$= 120 \times 15 - 240 \times 6$

$= 1800 - 1440$

$= 360$

Lesson 7.2 Assignment

NAME_____ DATE _____

Getting to the Root of It
Exploring Squares, Cubes, and Roots

1. Rika has spent years saving fabric remnants from special events or memories in her life. She has fabric from her crib bedding, her favorite baby blanket, and from many outfits that she wore for special occasions. She would like to make a quilt, so she has cut the fabric into 256 squares each measuring 6 inches by 6 inches.

   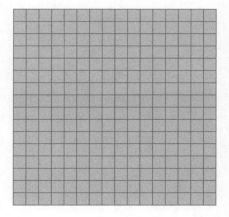

   a. What is the area of one quilt square? Show your work.

   b. Rika uses all 256 squares to make the square quilt shown. What is the area of the quilt? Show your work.

   c. How long is one side of Rika's quilt? Show your work.

2. Rika cuts 256 six-inch squares on the diagonal so she can make a complex quilt. What is the area of the triangle that results from cutting a quilt square on the diagonal? Explain your reasoning.

a. Rika then arranges the triangles of fabric into a new square. The long side of each triangle is the side of the square. What is the area of the new square? Explain your reasoning.

b. What is the side length of the new quilt square to the nearest tenth of an inch? Show your work.

c. How many of the larger quilt squares can Rika make from her 256 original squares? Explain your reasoning.

7

NAME_____ **DATE** _____

d. Rika wants her quilt to be square. Should she use all 128 of her larger quilt squares to make her quilt? Why or why not? Explain your reasoning.

3. Rika asks her husband to make her a cedar box in which she can keep her new quilt as well as other treasured mementos she has saved. In order to fit the quilt, he makes each side of the box 2 feet long.

a. What is the volume of the cedar box in cubic feet?

b. One of Rika's good friends sees the finished box in Rika's house. She asks Rika's husband if he could make her one, only larger. She decides she wants the volume of her cubic box to be 27 cubic feet. How long must Rika's husband make each side of the box?

c. Rika's husband decides that he will start a side business and sell the cubic cedar boxes. In order to get an idea of what to charge, he researches similar cedar boxes to see the prices they are sold at. The closest one he can find to his box is 20 cubic feet in volume. How long are the sides of this box? Estimate the answer to the nearest tenth.

d. Rika wants a box that is double the volume of her current box. She tells her husband all he needs to do is double the length of each of the sides of her current box. Is she correct? Explain your answer.

Lesson 7.3 Assignment

NAME_____ DATE _____

Things That Vary
Understanding Variables

1. The Little Dawgs Youth Football Club is holding a fundraiser for their organization. They are selling books of pizza coupons. For every book that the members sell, the club will make $2.50.

   a. Complete the table to determine the total number of coupon books the members sold.

Total Amount of Money Made	Amount Made for Each Coupon Book Sold	Number of Coupon Books Sold
$812.50	$2.50	
$1082.50	$2.50	
$1175.00	$2.50	

   b. What quantity or quantities changed? What quantity or quantities remained the same?

   c. Write a sentence to describe how to calculate the number of coupon books sold given the total amount of money made.

   d. Write an algebraic expression that represents the total number of coupon books sold for any amount of money made. Let m represent the total amount of money made.

2. The president of a club is trying to determine how many books he wants each member to sell in order to have enough money for the upcoming season. He decides to calculate the amount of money made dependent on how many books they sell. Complete the table to determine the amount of money the club will make.

Amount Made for Each Coupon Book Sold	Number of Coupon Books Sold	Total Amount of Money Made
$2.50	375	
$2.50	450	
$2.50	500	

a. What quantity or quantities changed? What quantity or quantities remained the same?

b. Write a sentence to describe how to calculate the total amount of money the club will make given the number of coupon books that were sold.

c. Write an equation to describe the situation in part (b). Let *n* represent the number of coupon books sold and *m* represent the total amount of money made.

d. The members of the club were able to sell 530 coupon books. The president of the club wanted to make $1400. Did the members sell enough books? Explain your reasoning.

7

NAME_____ **DATE** _____

3. A club already has 32 uniforms from last year. They aren't sure how many players they will have this year. Complete the table to determine how many new uniforms they will need to buy.

Total Number of Players	Number of Uniforms Owned By the Club	Number of Uniforms Needed
41		
44		
49		

a. Write a sentence to describe how to calculate the number of uniforms the club will need.

b. Write an algebraic expression to determine the number of uniforms needed if they currently have 32 uniforms. Let p represent the total number of players.

c. Use your expression to determine the number of uniforms needed if there are a total of 45 players.

Lesson 7.4 Assignment

NAME_____ DATE _____

What's My Number?
Writing Algebraic Expressions

Sheldon Elementary School has a school store that is open every Thursday. It sells many items including folders, pencils, erasers, and novelty items. The Parent Association at the school is in charge of buying the items for the store.

1. One popular item at the store is scented pencils. The pencils come in packs of 24 from the retailer.

   a. How many pencils will they have available to sell if they buy 2 packs from the retailer?

   b. How many pencils will they have available to sell if they buy 6 packs from the retailer?

   c. How many pencils will they have available to sell if they buy 9 packs from the retailer?

   d. Write a sentence to describe how you can determine the amount of pencils available to sell for any number of packs purchased.

   e. Write an algebraic expression that represents the total number of pencils they will have available to sell. Let p represent the number of packs of pencils they purchase from the retailer.

7

2. Another popular item at the school store is animal-themed folders. Each pack of folders contains 6 folders. They have 4 packs in the store currently and would like to order more.

   a. How many folders do they currently have?

   b. How many folders will they have if they order 2 more packs?

   c. How many folders will they have if they order 4 more packs?

   d. Write an algebraic expression that represents the total number of folders they will have in the store. Let x represent the number of packs of folders they buy.

   e. State the numerical coefficient and the constant in the expression from part (d).

   f. Write the meaning of the algebraic expression from part (d) in two ways.

3. The latest fad is animal-shaped rubber bracelets. Because of their popularity, the Parent Association wants to buy packs of them in bulk. They decide to shop around to find the best price.

   a. Store A sells 24 packs for $47.76. What is the cost per pack?

NAME_____ DATE _____

b. Store B sells 24 packs for $48.00. What is the cost per pack?

c. Store C sells 24 packs for $46.80. What is the cost per pack?

d. Write an algebraic expression that represents the cost per pack of bracelets. Let c represent the cost of 24 packs.

e. Write the meaning of the algebraic expression from part (d). Then, evaluate the expression for $c = 49.20$. Explain your answer in terms of the cost per pack of bracelets.

4. The store decides to have a clearance sale the last week of school. The expression $14 - n$ represents the number of folders they have at the end of the sale.

   a. Write the meaning of the algebraic expression in two ways. Then, explain what the expression means in terms of the number of folders.

   b. Complete the table to represent the numbers of folders they could have left at the end of the sale.

n	$14 - n$
2	
5	
11	
13	
14	

Lesson 7.5 Assignment

NAME_____ DATE _____

Different Ways
Multiple Representations of Algebraic Expressions

1. Julia receives an allowance of $6 each week for doing chores around the house. She is saving her allowance so that she'll have some spending money for her summer vacation.

   a. Complete the table to show the total amount Julia will have saved at the end of each week.

Number of Weeks	Amount Saved (in dollars)
1	
2	
3	
4	
5	
6	

   b. Define a variable and then write an algebraic expression that describes the relationship between the number of weeks and the amount Julia has saved.

   c. How much will Julia have saved after 15 weeks? Explain your reasoning.

   d. How many weeks will it take for Julia to save $168? Explain your reasoning.

e. Use your table from part (a) to plot the points on the graph. Be sure to label the axes.

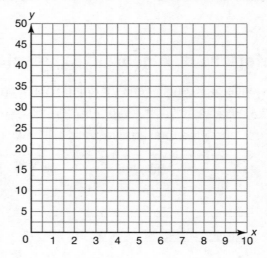

f. Does it make sense to connect the points on this graph? Explain why or why not.

2. Julia puts aside $60 of the money she has saved to use at the arcade at the beach. She likes a particular dance game that costs $3 every time that she plays.

   a. Define a variable for the quantity that changes. Then, write an algebraic expression for the amount of arcade money.

   b. How many times will she be able to play before she runs out of arcade money? Explain your reasoning.

NAME_____ DATE _____

c. Complete the table.

Number of Times Julia Plays the Game	Amount of Arcade Money Julia Has Left
4	
10	
18	
20	

d. Use your table to construct a graph. Be sure to label the axes.

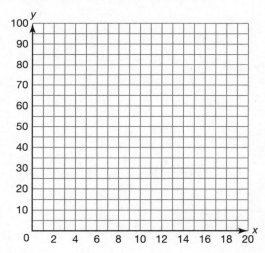

e. Does it make sense to connect the points on this graph? Explain why or why not.

7

7

NAME_____   DATE _____

There's More than One Way
Using Multiple Representations of Problems

1. Eddie Jung owns a water ice business. He has a portable water ice stand that he takes to various events. In the summer he can be found at many events including swim meets, carnivals, and baseball games. In order to make his popular treats, he uses an ice shaver to break off the ice from the blocks that he keeps in his stand. To keep the ice cold as well as use the ice shaver, he must use electricity from the venue where he is selling the water ice. Most venues charge him a flat fee of $100 plus $0.30 per minute for the electricity.

   a. Describe how Eddie would determine the amount he owes the venue at the end of an event.

   b. Eddie attends a swim meet in the rain. Due to the rain, his water ice does not sell well during the 2 hours he is there. How much will he owe the pool association? Use your verbal description from part (a) to solve.

   c. Complete the table that shows different amounts of time Eddie is at a venue and how much he owes.

Time at a Venue (minutes)	Amount Owed to a Venue (dollars)
30	
60	
90	
120	
150	
180	

d. Use your table from part (c) to plot the points on the graph.

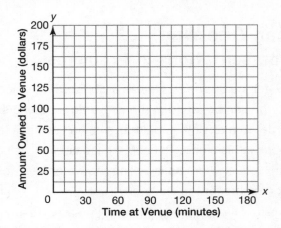

e. Define a variable for the amount of time Eddie uses electricity at the venues and write an expression for the amount of money he will owe to the venues.

f. What advantage(s), if any, does the expression provide that the verbal description, table, or graph does not?

7

NAME_____ DATE _____

The Parts of Cars You Don't See!
Relationships between Quantities

Answer each question using the scenario.

1. Odell and his family are visiting the Grand Canyon. Odell decides to drop a rock off the edge of a cliff. The distance the rock falls is 16 feet the first second, 48 feet the next second, 80 feet the third second, and so on.

   a. Write two sequences using the rock that Odell dropped.

   b. What is the third term of the second sequence?

   c. What are the two quantities that change?

   d. Which quantity depends on the other?

   e. Explain how you would determine the distance that the rock falls in the fourth and fifth seconds.

   f. Describe how to calculate the distance the rock falls in the tenth second.

8

2. Odell and his family are taking mule rides down the Grand Canyon. The price for the one-day mule ride is $150 per rider. Write two sequences that represent the mule rides.

a. What are the variable quantities in this situation? Include the units that are used to measure these quantities.

b. Which variable quantity depends on the other variable quantity?

c. Write an algebraic expression for the total cost, in dollars, for *n* riders.

d. If Odell has 5 people in his family, how much will the mule rides cost? Use the algebraic expression to solve.

e. The total mileage for the mule ride will be about 12 miles. The time to ride the trail will be *t* hours. Write an algebraic expression to represent the rate at which the riders will travel.

8

3. Identify the number of terms in each expression and then the terms themselves for each algebraic expression.

   a. $6y + 14$

   b. $7x - 3y + 12z$

   c. $104a + 224b$

Lesson 8.2 Assignment

NAME_____ DATE _____

Tile Work
Simplifying Algebraic Expressions

1. Natsu is in charge of building sets for his high school's musical production. The first set he is going to work on is constructing a wall of a living room. The director wants the wall to measure 15 feet wide by 8 feet tall. Natsu first needs to find the perimeter of the wall to build the frame.

   a. The perimeter is the sum of the lengths plus the sum of the widths, or $30 + 16$. Rewrite this expression to demonstrate the Commutative Property of Addition.

   b. The equation for calculating the perimeter of a rectangle is $P = 2l + 2w$, where l = length and w = width. Calculate the perimeter of the wall using this equation. Use the Order of Operations to solve.

   c. Rewrite the equation in a different way to demonstrate the Commutative Property of Multiplication.

8

d. The director wants two small 3-foot square windows in the wall. Natsu must now determine how much area there will be on the wall that needs to be painted. He needs to find the area of the wall and then subtract two times the area of one window, or $15 \times 8 - 2(3^2)$. Evaluate this expression using the Order of Operations.

2. Sadie is going to make a triangular platform as part of a set for her high school's musical production. The triangle will have a base length of 6 feet and the two sides will each measure 5 feet.

a. Write and solve the equation that represents the perimeter of the triangle.

b. Rewrite and solve an equivalent equation using the Commutative Property of Addition.

c. Sadie will cover the top of the triangular platform with artificial grass, so she needs to know the area of the triangle. The area of a triangle can be found using the equation $A = \frac{1}{2}bh$. The base of the triangle is 6 feet and the height is 4 feet. Find the area of the triangle using this equation.

NAME_____ DATE _____

    d. Write and solve an equivalent equation for the area using the Associative Property of Multiplication.

3. To help pay for sets, the director of a high school musical production has decided to increase the price of admission. He will charge $10 for students and $14 for adults for the Saturday night show.

    a. If x represents the number of student tickets purchased and y represents the number of adult tickets purchased, write an expression for the total amount of money they will make from Saturday night's show.

    b. Represent this algebraic expression using algebra tiles. Then sketch the model.

8

c. The director will charge less for the Saturday matinee show. He will charge $8 for students and $12 for adults. Write the expression for the total amount of money they will make from the matinee.

d. Represent this algebraic expression using algebra tiles. Then sketch the model.

e. Write the expression that represents the total amount of money they will bring in from both shows. Simplify the expression.

NAME_____ DATE _____

Blueprints to Floor Plans to Computers
Using the Distributive Property to Simplify Algebraic Expressions

1. Nelson is going on an overnight camping family reunion. He is in charge of bringing the wood for the campfire. He will start the fire with 6 logs and then will need about 3 logs for each hour the fire burns.

   a. Represent the number of logs he will use with an algebraic expression. Define your variable.

   b. Suppose the family decides to stay for 2 nights next year. Write the expression for the number of logs they would need for 2 nights.

   c. Simplify this expression. Create a model using your algebra tiles, and then sketch the model you create.

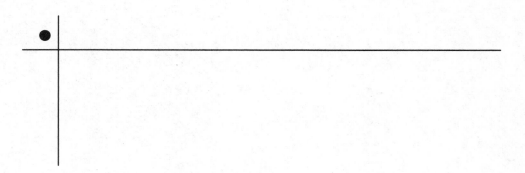

   d. Nelson's cousin believes they will need only one-third of the firewood Nelson brings for one night. Represent this as an expression. Then simplify the expression using a Distributive Property. State which Distributive Property you used.

8

e. There are several family members who will be visiting for the day only. The campground charges $6 per car, plus $2 per visitor. One of the families brings a coupon for $3 off their total fee. Write the expression that represents their total cost for the day. Define the variables.

f. The two oldest uncles at the reunion insist on paying the bill for the day visitors. They will split it equally. Represent the amount of money each uncle will pay as an expression. Then simplify the expression using a Distributive Property. State which Distributive Property you used.

NAME _____ **DATE** _____

Are They Saying the Same Thing?
Multiple Representations of Equivalent Expressions

1. Wan and Rosa are going on a road trip. The amount of money they have budgeted will pay for gas, lodging, food, and entertainment. Gas costs $3.15 per gallon. They have used 10 gallons of gas so far on their trip. They want to determine the total amount of money that will be spent on gas for the trip. Let g represent the number of additional gallons of gas they will use.

   a. Wan represents the total amount of money spent by the expression $3.15(g + 10)$. Describe the meaning of this expression in terms of the problem situation. Include a description for the units of each number or variable in the expression.

   b. Rosa represents the total amount of money spent by the expression $3.15g + 31.50$. Describe the meaning of this expression in terms of the problem situation. Include a description for the units of each number or variable in the expression.

   c. Complete the table.

Number of Additional Gallons of Gas, g	Wan's Expression $3.15(g + 10)$	Rosa's Expression $3.15g + 31.50$
10		
25		
35		
50		

8

d. Are the two expressions equivalent? Use your results from the table to explain your reasoning.

e. Describe how you could use the graphing function of a graphing calculator to show that both expressions are equivalent.

2. Wan and Rosa started with $800 in spending money for a trip. Let x represent the amount of money they spent on food already. Then the amount of money they have left is $800 - x$. Wan decides that she wants to split up the remaining money equally between them. Wan claims they will each get $400 - x$ dollars. Rosa disputes this and says they will each get $\frac{1}{2}(800 - x)$. Wan says this is the same as $400 - x$.

   a. Determine if the two expressions are equivalent. Choose 3 different values for x and complete the table.

x	Wan's Expression $400 - x$	Rosa's Expression $\frac{1}{2}(800 - x)$

   b. Whose expression is correct? Explain your reasoning.

NAME_____ DATE _____

3. Partway into a trip, Wan and Rosa stop at the home of their friend, Teresa. Teresa decides to join them on their road trip. The three girls decide to take turns driving and split up the total driving time equally among them. So far, since picking up Teresa, they have traveled for 8 hours.

a. If they travel an additional 7 hours, how many hours will each friend drive?

b. If they travel an additional 16 hours, how many hours will each friend drive?

c. Write an expression that represents the number of hours each friend will drive. Let h represent the number of additional hours they drive.

8

Lesson 8.5 Assignment

Like and Unlike
Combining Like Terms

1. Use algebra tiles to model algebraic expressions.

   a. Represent the algebraic expression $3x + 2y + y^2 + 5x$ using algebra tiles and the operation symbols. Sketch the model.

   b. Rearrange the tiles in part (a) so that there are only 3 terms. Sketch your new model, including the operation symbols.

   c. Write the algebraic expression represented.

   d. Could you rearrange the tiles so there are only 2 terms? Explain your reasoning.

8

2. The algebraic expression $4x + 3(x + 2)$ is represented with algebra tiles and the operation symbols.

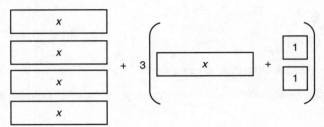

a. Use the distributive property to rewrite the expression without parentheses.

$4x + 3(x + 2) = $ _____

b. Model your new expression using algebra tiles and operation symbols.

c. Rearrange the tiles to reduce the number of terms to the fewest possible terms.

d. Write the algebraic expression represented.

Lesson 8.6 Assignment

NAME_____ DATE _____

DVDs and Songs: Fun with Expressions
Using Algebraic Expressions to Analyze and Solve Problems

At the end of each school year, Evan cleans out all of the school supplies that have collected in his desk. He can't believe how much stuff is in there this year! He has 4 times as many markers as he has pencils. He has 3 more highlighters than he has markers. He has twice as many pens as he has highlighters.

1. Suppose Evan found 5 pencils in his desk.

   a. Determine the number of markers that are in his desk. Explain your reasoning.

   b. Determine the number of highlighters that are in his desk. Explain your reasoning.

   c. Determine the number of pens that are in his desk. Explain your reasoning.

   d. Determine the total number of writing utensils that are in his desk. Explain your reasoning.

8

2. Suppose Evan found 78 pens in his desk.

   a. Determine the number of highlighters that are in his desk. Explain your reasoning.

   b. Determine the number of markers that are in his desk. Explain your reasoning.

   c. Determine the number of pencils that are in his desk. Explain your reasoning.

   d. Determine the total number of writing utensils that are in his desk. Explain your reasoning.

3. Let p represent the number of pencils that Evan has in his desk.

   a. Write an algebraic expression that represents the number of markers in Evan's desk.

NAME_____ DATE _____

b. Write an algebraic expression that represents the number of highlighters in Evan's desk.

c. Write an algebraic expression that represents the number of pens in Evan's desk.

d. Write an algebraic expression that represents the total number of writing utensils in Evan's desk.

e. Simplify the expression you wrote in part (d).

f. Use the simplified expression from part (e) to determine the total number of writing utensils in Evan's desk if there are 8 pencils.

g. Use your expression from part (e) to determine the total number of writing utensils in Evan's desk if there are 12 pencils.

4. Let h represent the number of highlighters in Evan's desk.

a. Write an algebraic expression that represents the number of markers in Evan's desk.

b. Write an algebraic expression that represents the number of pencils in Evan's desk.

c. Write an algebraic expression that represents the number of p ens in Evan's desk.

d. Write an algebraic expression that represents the total number of writing utensils in Evan's desk.

NAME_____ DATE _____

Call to Order
Inequalities

1. Mr. James is the oldest man living in Smalltown. The children in his neighborhood like to try to guess his age. One day, Mr. James tells the children that he is at least as old as the number of cents in 9 dimes and 2 pennies.

   a. What is the value of 9 dimes and 2 pennies? Show your work.

   b. Plot and label your answer to part (a) on the number line.

   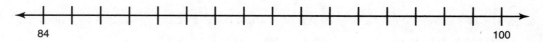

   84   100

   c. If you were to graph Mr. James' age on the number line, would it be to the right or the left of the point you plotted in part (b)? Explain your reasoning.

   d. Write an inequality that corresponds with the statement Mr. James made about his age. Use *j* as your variable. Explain how you determined which symbol to use.

   e. Describe the solution set for the inequality in part (d).

   f. Sketch the graph of the inequality you wrote in part (d).

   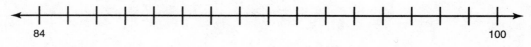

   84   100

9

   g. Do you have enough information to determine Mr. James' age? Explain your reasoning.

2. Ms. Carmichael says that she is at least 65 years old. She asks Cassandra and Cho to guess her age. Cassandra guesses 68, and Cho guesses 64. Who has the more reasonable guess? Explain your reasoning.

   a. Ms. Carmichael says that she is younger than the number of minutes in 1 hour and 10 minutes. How many hours are in 1 hour and 10 minutes? Show your work.

   b. Write an inequality that corresponds with the statement Ms. Carmichael made about her age in part (a). Use c as your variable. Explain how you determined which symbol to use.

   c. Sketch the graph of the inequality you wrote in part (b).

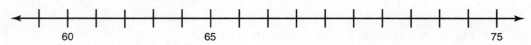

   d. Make a guess for Ms. Carmichael's age. Explain why you chose your answer.

Lesson 9.2   Assignment

NAME_____ **DATE** _____

Opposites Attract to Maintain a Balance
Solving One-Step Equations Using Addition and Subtraction

1. Ms. DeAngel teaches third grade. She is ordering supplies for the new school year. She wants every student to have a sturdy folder in which they can transport papers back and forth to school. She has 16 students in her class this year and has 3 folders left from last year. She wants to determine how many folders she will need to order. The balance shown represents this situation.

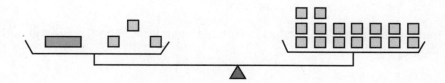

   a. Determine what will balance 1 rectangle. Describe your strategy.

   b. Write an equation that represents the pan balance. Let ▭ represent the variable *x*, or the number of folders Ms. DeAngel needs to order. Let ☐ represent 1 folder.

   c. Consider the equation that you wrote in part (b). State the inverse operation needed to isolate the variable. Then, solve the equation. Show your work. Finally, check to see if the value of your solution maintains balance in the original equation.

   d. What does your solution in part (c) mean in terms of the problem? Does it match the answer you got earlier for the balance problem?

2. Ms. DeAngel orders writing journals for each of her students. She has 28 students in her class. After she gives one journal to each of her students, she realizes that she has 7 journals left. She writes the following equation to represent her situation.

$$w - 28 = 7$$

a. What does the variable in Ms. DeAngel's equation represent?

b. State the inverse operation needed to isolate the variable. Then, solve the equation. Show your work.

c. Check to see if the value of your solution maintains balance in the original equation.

d. What does your solution in part (b) mean in terms of the problem?

e. Using your solution in part (b), write a different equation for this situation using the Subtraction Property of Equality.

NAME_____   DATE _____

Statements of Equality Redux
Solving One-Step Equations with Multiplication and Division

1. Stephanie has 60 party favors that she wants to divide among her guests so that each one receives the same number of favors. There are 15 guests at Stephanie's party. The balance represents this situation.

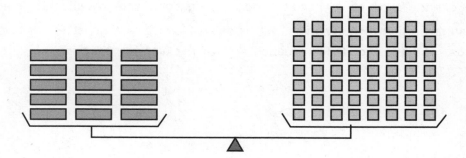

   a. Determine what will balance 1 rectangle. Describe your strategy.

   b. Write an equation that represents the pan balance. Let ▬ represent the variable x, or the number of party favors each guest will receive. Let ☐ represent 1 party favor.

   c. Consider the equation that you wrote in part (b). State the inverse operation needed to isolate the variable. Then, solve the equation. Make sure that you show your work. Finally, check to see if the value of your solution maintains balance in the original equation.

9

d. What does your solution in part (c) mean in terms of the problem? Does it match the answer you got earlier for the balance problem?

2. Bertrand invites 21 people to his party and wants to give each guest 3 party favors. If n is the total number of party favors he will need to order, the equation that represents this situation is $\frac{n}{21} = 3$.

   a. If Bertrand orders 58 party favors, will he be able to give each guest 3 party favors? In other words, is 58 a solution to the equation $\frac{n}{21} = 3$? Explain your reasoning.

   b. If the Bertrand orders 62 party favors, will he be able to give each guest 3 party favors? In other words, is 62 a solution to the equation $\frac{n}{21} = 3$? Explain your reasoning.

c. How many party favors does Bertrand need to order? Use the equation to determine the solution. State the inverse operation needed to isolate the variable. Then, solve the equation. Make sure to show your work. Finally, check to see if the value of your solution maintains balance in the original equation.

d. Using your solution in part (c), write a different equation for this situation using the Division Property of Equality.

9

Lesson 9.4 Assignment

NAME_____ DATE _____

There Are Many Ways . . .
Representing Situations in Multiple Ways

1. A shuttle space suit, including the life support system, weighs about 310 pounds.

   a. If an astronaut weighs 183 pounds, how much will she weigh when she is wearing her shuttle suit? Show your work.

   b. Define variables for the weight of an astronaut and the weight of an astronaut wearing her shuttle suit.

   c. Write an equation that models the relationship between these variables.

   d. Use the equation from part (c) to complete the table below.

Weight of Astronaut without Shuttle Suit (pounds)	Weight of Astronaut with Shuttle Suit (pounds)
183	
162	
	488
200	
	437
	456

e. Use the table to complete the graph.

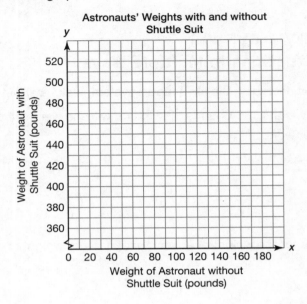

Astronauts' Weights with and without
Shuttle Suit

Weight of Astronaut with Shuttle Suit (pounds)

Weight of Astronaut without
Shuttle Suit (pounds)

f. Does it make sense to connect the points on this graph? Explain your reasoning.

2. The gravitational pull of the moon is not as great as that on Earth. In fact, if a person checks their weight on the Moon, it will be only $\frac{1}{6}$ of their weight on Earth.

a. If a person weighs 186 pounds on Earth, how much will he weigh on the Moon? Show your work.

b. Define variables for the weight of a person on Earth and the weight of a person on the Moon.

c. Write an equation that models the relationship between these variables.

NAME_____ DATE _____

d. Use the equation from part (c) to complete the table below.

Weight on Earth (pounds)	Weight on the Moon (pounds)
186	
168	
	29
198	
	21
	24

e. Use the table to complete the graph.

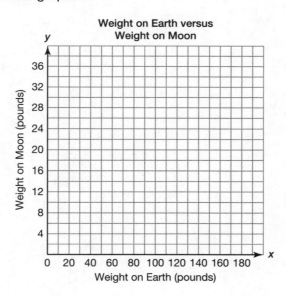

Weight on Earth versus Weight on Moon

f. Does it make sense to connect the points on this graph? Explain your reasoning.

9

Lesson 9.5 Assignment

NAME_____ DATE _____

Measuring Short
Using Multiple Representations to Solve Problems

1. Lashawna works at the local candy shop. The bulk candy is sold by the pound. Customers place the candy they would like to buy in a plastic bucket, and then Lashawna weighs it to determine how much the customer owes. Before calculating the price, Lashawna must subtract the weight of the plastic bucket. The candy bucket weighs 0.72 pound.

   a. When Lashawna weighs Ty's bucket of candy, the total weight is 2.84 pounds. How many pounds of candy does Ty have in his bucket? Show your work.

   b. Define variables for the total weight and the weight of the candy.

   c. Write an equation that models the relationship between these variables.

   d. Use the equation from part (c) to complete the table below.

Total Weight (pounds)	Weight of Candy (pounds)
2.84	
3.00	
	0.71
0.98	
	1.71
	1.13

e. Use the table to complete the graph.

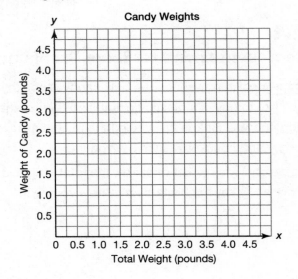

Candy Weights

f. Does it make sense to connect the points on this graph? Explain your reasoning.

2. Lashawna is packaging some of the bulk candy for a sale.

a. If the price per pound is $3.98, how many pounds of candy are in a package that costs $9.95? Show your work.

b. Define variables for the total cost and the weight of the candy.

c. Write an equation that models the relationship between these variables.

d. Use the equation from part (c) to complete the table below. Round the total cost to the nearest hundredth, if necessary.

Total Cost (dollars)	Weight of Candy (pounds)
	2.50
	3.20
4.98	
	1.97
9.47	
13.93	

e. Use the table to complete the graph.

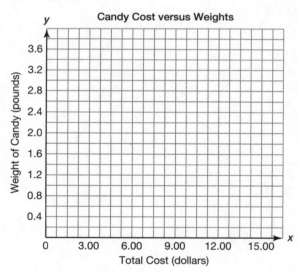

Candy Cost versus Weights

f. Does it make sense to connect the points on this graph? Explain your reasoning.

9

NAME_____   DATE _____

Variables and More Variables
The Many Uses of Variables in Mathematics

1. You can write equations with variables to represent the following scenarios. For each scenario, describe how the variables are used: variables as unknowns, variables that represent all numbers, variables in formulas, or variables that vary. Explain your reasoning.

   a. Find the circumference of a circle given the circle's diameter.

   b. The product of any number and 1 is that number.

   c. To find the number of inches in a given number of feet, multiply the number of feet by 12.

   d. A quantity minus 42.1 is equal to 13.7.

2. The equations listed in the first column of the table represent different ways variables are used. Categorize each equation by placing an "X" in the column that describes the way in which variables are used in that equation. Explain your reasoning in the column provided.

Equation	Variables as Unknowns	Variables that Vary	Explain Your Reasoning
$3.2x = y$			
$75 = 15b$			
$\dfrac{t}{8} = 16$			
$9\dfrac{1}{8} - d = e$			
$p + 4 = 25$			

NAME_____ DATE _____

a. Choose one of the equations from the table above in which the variable is an unknown. Solve for the variable. Show your work.

b. Choose one of the equations from the table above in which the variables vary. Choose a value for one of the variables and solve for the other variable. Show your work.

3. The equation $A = l \times w$ is the formula for the area of a rectangle, where l represents the length and w represents the width. Find the area of a rectangle with a length of 8 units and a width of 3 units. Show your work.

a. Can the formula for the area of a rectangle also be categorized as an equation in which the variables vary? Explain your reasoning.

4. Explain why the following is an example of an equation in which the variables represent all numbers.

$$\text{For any number } p,\ p + 0 = p.$$

Quantities that Change
Independent and Dependent Variables

1. Jana is a runner. When she is training for a race, she averages a speed of 8 miles per hour.

   a. How many miles can Jana run in 2 hours? Show your work.

   b. Define variables for each changing quantity and write an equation to represent the situation.

   c. Identify the independent and dependent variables in this situation. Explain how you determined your answer.

   d. Use your equation from part (b) and your answer to part (c) to complete the table. Remember to choose reasonable values for your independent variable.

	Independent Quantity	Dependent Quantity
Quantity Name		
Unit of Measure		
Variable		

e. Use the table to complete the graph. Remember to label your axes.

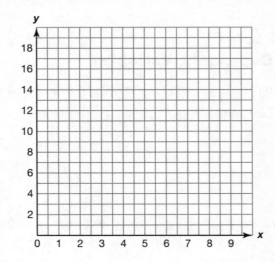

f. Explain how you knew which variable to graph on each axis.

g. Does it make sense to connect the points on this graph? Explain your reasoning.

2. Rewrite the equation $8h = m$ to solve for h.

NAME_____ DATE _____

3. With the equation written in this form, which variable is independent and which is dependent? Explain your reasoning.

9

Lesson 10.1 Assignment

NAME_____ DATE _____

What, Me Negative?
Introduction to Negative Integers

Use the scenario to answer each question.

Roller coasters have a rich history in the United States, and engineers are constantly working to make the next "best" ride. Although technology, such as steel, has allowed coasters to become higher and faster, many riders still appreciate the experience of a wooden coaster. One newer trend is a hybrid coaster that uses both steel and wood. One such hybrid coaster, the Ravine Flyer II, also takes advantage of terrain to make the ride more exciting. Although the Ravine Flyer II is only 80 feet high, it follows the line of a cliff in order to drop to −35 feet (0 represents ground level).

1. Plot the highest and lowest points of the roller coaster on the number line shown.

100

0

−50

   a. Explain why a vertical number line better represents the problem context than a horizontal number line.

   b. How many total feet does the roller coaster drop?

2. The Monster is a roller coaster that uses a similar design to the Ravine Flyer II. The Ravine Flyer II has a height of 80 feet and drops to -35 feet. The Monster reaches a height of 120 feet, but then drops to -25 feet. Order the highest and lowest points of the two roller coasters from least to greatest.

3. An amusement park wants a company to design a coaster that rises 60 feet above ground then drops the same distance below ground through a tunnel. Represent the underground depth with an integer, and explain its relationship with the above ground height.

10

NAME_____   DATE _____

Number Sets
Number Systems

Nadine is doing research on the tundra for her science class. She collects facts about the region for her report.

1. Write all the sets of numbers to which each value belongs.

  a. The tundra covers about $\frac{1}{5}$ of Earth's surface.

  b. The average annual temperature is $-18°$ Fahrenheit.

  c. There are 48 varieties of land mammals found in the tundra region.

  d. The permafrost is a layer of frozen soil that is located below Earth's surface at -1476 feet.

  e. During the summer months, the low temperature averages about 37.4°F.

2. Nadine collects data about some of the animals that live in the tundra. Determine a rational number between each pair of rational numbers.

  a. Adult male polar bears measure 2.5 to 3 meters tall.

  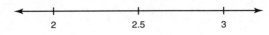

  b. Newborn polar bear cubs' weights range from $\frac{3}{8}$ to $\frac{1}{2}$ kilograms.

  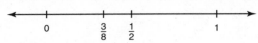

c. The polar bear mother's milk is very rich in calories; anywhere from 0.31 to 0.32 of the milk is composed of fat.

d. The percent of change of the Alaskan polar bear population in the past year was between −0.33 and −0.32.

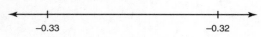

3. Nadine discovered the following information about the climate. Place each value on the number line.

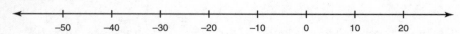

a. The lowest temperature recorded was −52.5° Celsius.

b. The highest temperature recorded was +18.3° Celsius.

c. The amount of precipitation, mostly in the form of snow, averages about $9\frac{3}{4}$ inches per year.

NAME_____ DATE _____

Ordering and Absolute Value
Ordering the Rational Numbers

Use the scenario to answer each question.

1. Julio is a wrestler for his high school wrestling team in the winter. Although he does not wrestle in the 12 weeks of summer, his coach would like him to stay around 140 pounds so that he doesn't have to work so hard during the season to stay in his weight class. Julio charted his weight over the summer by listing the differences his weight was from 140 pounds. He uses negative numbers when his weight was under 140 pounds and positive numbers when his weight was above 140 pounds. The chart shows his results.

Week	1	2	3	4	5	6	7	8	9	10	11	12
Weight Differential	+4.5	+2.1	−1.5	−0.5	−2.5	+1.5	−3.75	−2.8	0	+1.3	−1.5	−5

a. Plot the weight differences from Week 2 and Week 7 on the number line.
Then, insert a >, <, or = symbol to make the number sentence true.

2.1 ◯ −3.75

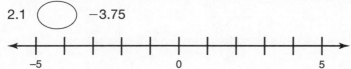

b. Plot the weight difference from week 3 and week 4 on the number line.
Then, insert a >, <, or = symbol to make the number sentence true.

−1.5 ◯ −0.5

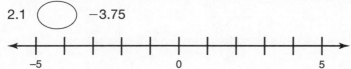

c. Order all of the weight differences from least to greatest.

d. Was the amount of weight change in week 4 more or less than the amount of weight change in week 8? Insert a $>$, $<$, or $=$ symbol to make the statement true. Explain your answer.

$|-0.5|$ $\bigcirc$ $|-2.8|$

e. Was the amount of weight change in week 6 more or less than the amount of weight change in week 11? Insert a $>$, $<$, or $=$ symbol to make the statement true.

$|+1.5|$ $\bigcirc$ $|-1.5|$

f. Determine the difference between the weight changes from week 7 to week 10. Use absolute values to determine the difference.

g. Determine the difference between the weight changes from week 8 to week 12. Use absolute values to determine the difference.

2. The table shown tracks Julio's weight changes that he reports to his coach for the first 4 weeks of school. Complete the table to explain the changes.

Situation	Absolute Value Statement	Rational Number
His weight went from 140 to 135 pounds.	His weight fell by 5 pounds.	
His weight went from 135 pounds to 141 pounds.		6 lb
His weight went from 141 pounds to 140.5 pounds.		
His weight went from 140.5 pounds to 139 pounds.		

NAME_____   DATE _____

Elevators, Making Money Redux, and Water Level
Solving Problems with Rational Numbers

Use the scenario to answer each question.

1. Weather experts collect many types of data to study and analyze. One area of interest to many meteorologists is extreme temperature changes. The interior West of North America experiences great temperature changes due to Chinook Winds. The table shows extreme temperature rises in three cities as well as the date and time period.

Place	Granville, ND	Fort Assiniboine, MT	Spearfish, SD
Date	Feb. 21, 1918	Jan. 19, 1892	Jan. 22, 1943
Time Period	12 hours	15 minutes	2 minutes
Temperature Change	From −33°F to 50°F	From −5°F to 37°F	From −4°F to 45°F

Source: Infoplease.© 2000-2007

a. How much did the temperature rise in Granville, ND? Write an equation for this situation and calculate the change.

b. How much did the temperature rise in Fort Assiniboine, MT? Write an equation for this situation and calculate the change.

c. How much did the temperature rise in Spearfish, SD? Write an equation for this situation and calculate the change.

2. An interesting day of temperature changes occurred in Rapid City, South Dakota on January 22, 1943. The table shows the temperature changes that happened throughout the day.

Time	Temperature (°C)
10:30 AM	−6.7
10:35 AM	13.3
12:00 PM	15.6
12:05 PM	−10.6
12:35 PM	−9.4
12:40 PM	10
2:20 PM	14.4
2:25 PM	−8.3

Source: http://www.blackhillsweather.com/chinook.html

a. Between which two times did the temperature change the most? Write an equation for this situation and calculate the change.

b. Between which two times did the temperature change the least? Write an equation for this situation and calculate the change.

NAME_____ DATE _____

   c. How much did the temperature change between 12:35 PM and 12:40 PM? Write an equation for this situation and calculate the change.

   d. How much did the temperature change between 2:20 PM and 2:25 PM? Write an equation for this situation and calculate the change.

10

10

NAME_____   **DATE** _____

Four Quadrants
Extending the Coordinate Plane

The coordinate system shown represents a map of Paul's neighborhood. Each square represents one city block. Paul's house is located at point *A*, which is the origin, or the point (0, 0). The other points represent the following locations.

B – USA Bank

C – Paul's friend Franco's house

D – Gray's Grocery Store

E – Post Office

F – Edward Middle School

G – Playground

H – Smiles Orthodontics

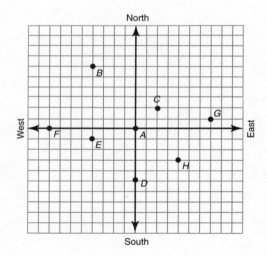

1. Explain how Paul can get to the given destination from his house if he were to first walk east or west and then walk north or south. Then, determine the coordinates of the destination point and the quadrant in which the point is located.

   a. USA Bank

   b. Smiles Orthodontics

   c. His friend Franco's house

   d. The Playground

   e. The Post Office

2. Use the coordinate grid to determine the distance from USA Bank to the Post Office. Remember that each square represents 1 city block.

3. Identify the ordered pairs associated with *B* and *E*. Describe how the ordered pairs for *B* and *E* are similar.

NAME_____ **DATE** _____

4. Use the *y*-coordinates of points *B* and *E*. Calculate $|6| + |-1|$.

5. How can an absolute value equation help you calculate the distance from one point to another on the coordinate plane when the points are on the same vertical line?

11

NAME_____   **DATE**_____

Geometry and Graphs
Graphing Geometric Figures

1. Johanna's house is represented as point *A* on the coordinate system shown. Johanna leaves her house to run some errands, and she returns home later that day. The following points represent the location of each stop that Johanna made. Plot and label the locations on the coordinate system. Draw a line from point to point as Johanna makes her journey, then describe the figure created by the path that she traveled.

   Start: *A* (0, 5)

   B (1, 3)

   C (4, 3)

   D (2, 1)

   E (4, –3)

   F (0, –1)

   G (–4, –3)

   H (–2, 1)

   I (–4, 3)

   J (–1, 3)

   Finish: *A* (0, 5)

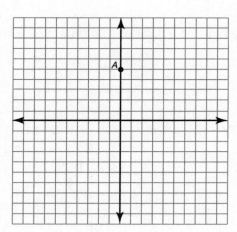

2. On the coordinate plane, the points *A* (–3, –3) and *B* (4, –3) are plotted to form segment *AB*.

   a. Plot and label point *C* so that a right triangle is formed. Plot and label point *D* so that an acute triangle is formed.

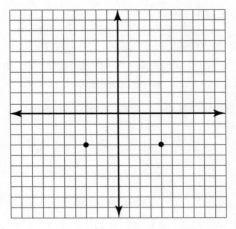

   b. How do you know that the triangles are drawn correctly?

3. Plot and identify 4 points that are the vertices of a trapezoid. Explain how you know it is drawn correctly.

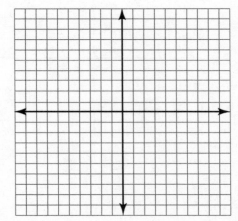

Lesson 11.3 Assignment

NAME_____ DATE _____

Water, Water Everywhere
Solving Problems with Multiple Representations

1. Sarina's favorite pet, Bruno the dog, just got bad news from the veterinarian—he has to go on a diet! Sarina puts Bruno on a diet plan of daily exercise and a special type of dog food. She estimates that Bruno will lose $1\frac{1}{2}$ pounds per week.

   a. How many pounds does Sarina estimate Bruno will lose in 2 weeks?

   b. How many pounds does Sarina estimate Bruno will lose in $8\frac{1}{2}$ weeks?

   c. What quantities are changing in this situation?

   d. Define variables for the independent and dependent quantities.

   e. Write an equation for this situation. (Since he is losing weight, the number of pounds he loses will be defined as a negative value.)

f. Complete the table. Then, graph the equation using the values from the table.

Time, w (in weeks)	Change in Weight, p (in pounds)
2	
5	
8.5	
10	

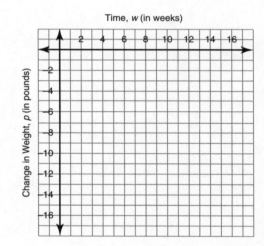

Time, w (in weeks)

Change in Weight, p (in pounds)

g. How much weight will Bruno have lost when he goes back to his veterinarian in 12 weeks?

NAME_____ DATE _____

2. The following graph shows the average temperature, in degrees Celsius, in Fairbanks, Alaska. The x-axis represents time in days from January 1, and the y-axis represents degrees Celsius.

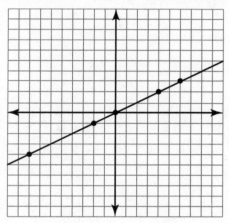

11

a. Create a table of values for the points on the graph.

x	y

b. Describe the meaning of the leftmost point.

c. Describe the meaning of the point second from the left.

d. Describe the meaning of the rightmost point.

e. At what rate did the temperature increase?

f. Define variables for the quantities that are changing, and write an equation for this situation.

Lesson 11.4   Assignment

NAME_____ DATE _____

Every Graph Tells a Story!
Interpreting Graphs

1. Ms. Grayson teaches an Advanced Placement class during Period 4. At the end of the year, these students take an Advanced Placement test. The graph shows the number of students who passed the test each year.

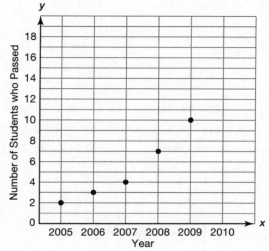

a. What relationship does the graph show?

b. What information is represented on the x-axis?

c. What information is represented on the y-axis?

d. In which year did the most students pass the Advanced Placement test? How do you know? How many students passed?

e. In which year did the fewest number of students pass the Advanced Placement test? How do you know? How many students passed?

f. Explain in your own words the relationship between the year and the number of students who passed the Advanced Placement test.

g. To teach the Advanced Placement course, Ms. Grayson depends on funding from the state for her course materials. The graph shows the amount of state funding for honors materials that the school has received over the past three decades. Describe the graph.

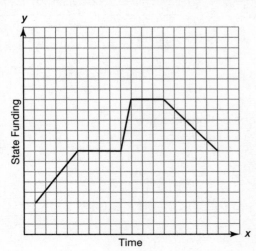

NAME _____   DATE _____

2. To keep her students relaxed and focused during the Advanced Placement test, Ms. Grayson puts small bowls of candy on each of their desks. Each graph shows the amount of candy in a student's bowl during the testing period. Write a short story to describe the graph.

a.

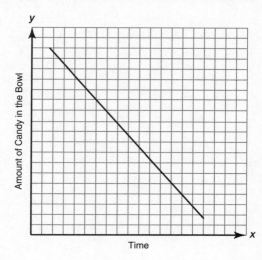

b.

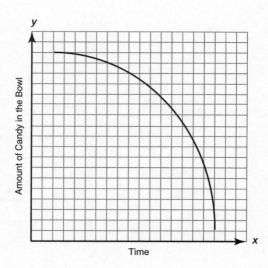

c.

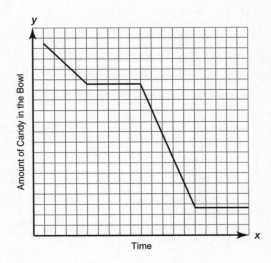

d.

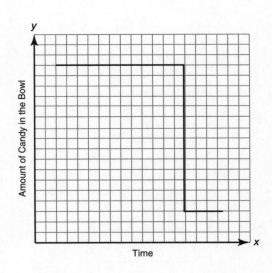

NAME_____ DATE _____

Customary to Whom?
Customary Measurement

Frederick has decided to put a rectangular addition onto his house. He will do most of the work by himself, so it will be necessary for him to be familiar with all kinds of measurements. Answer each question.

1. Frederick must measure and stake out the distance the addition will be from the house. Choose the appropriate customary unit of measure that he should use when measuring this distance.

   a. After he decides on the size of the addition, Frederick will pour concrete to create the base of the foundation. After it dries, he wants to seal the concrete with some paint. Choose the appropriate customary unit of measure he should use when he purchases the paint.

   b. After Frederick has built the framework of the addition, he will need help lifting the framing into place. Choose the appropriate customary unit of measure Frederick should use to describe to his friends the amount they will be lifting.

2. Marcy is going to go shopping for the furnishings that will go inside a new addition to her house. She did not take measurements, so she must make some approximations in the store. Choose the most appropriate measurement for each of the following.

   a. The length of the addition, which is needed to order carpeting

   2 mi   20 ft   2 yd   7 in.

   b. The weight of a print for the wall, which is needed to pick the correct hook size

   3 lb   3 oz   4 t   6 qt

c. The capacity of the floor planter needed for an indoor plant she bought

2 fl oz   1 c   2 pt   2 gal

3. When Frederick needs supplies from the store, he sometimes sends his nephew Jonah to get them. Unfortunately, there are times when the units Frederick gives him are not the units that the store uses, so Jonah must convert the measurements. Help Jonah make the necessary conversions.

a. Jonah needs to buy 4 yards of electrical wire. The store only sells the wire by the foot. How many feet does Jonah need?

b. Jonah needs to buy 14 quarts of liquid nails. The store only sells liquid nails by the gallon. How many gallons does Jonah need?

4. Keenan wants to make sure he has enough homemade iced tea for everyone. He makes 2 gallons of iced tea. He wants to have enough for 40 cups of tea. Did he make enough?

Lesson 12.2 Assignment

NAME_____ DATE _____

It's All Based on Powers of 10!
Metric Measurement

Jin Lee is the head zookeeper at the Perry Park Zoo. One of the largest and most popular attractions at this zoo is the penguin house, where Jin Lee spends a lot of his time. Jin Lee uses the metric system of measurement for many aspects of his job.

1. Choose the appropriate metric unit of measure that Jin Lee should use in each case.

   a. The amount of water that is needed for the penguin swimming tank

   b. The mass of each penguin

   c. The height of each penguin

2. The part of Jin Lee's job that he loves the most is the educational lectures he gives to students who are visiting for the day. The following questions are examples of some of the questions he asks during the lecture. Choose the most appropriate answer and explain your reasoning.

   a. What is the maximum distance a penguin can dive?

   10 mm   40 cm   550 m   2000 km

b. What is the average amount of fish a penguin consumes in one day?

0.9 kg   10 mg   15 g   1000 kg

c. What is the average length of a penguin's egg?

4 mm   12 cm   2 km   4 m

3. Jin Lee has a volunteer help weigh a penguin's egg. The egg weighs 0.15 kilogram. Is this more or less than the average egg weight of 145 grams? Explain.

4. The zoo has decided to grant Jin Lee's request to expand the penguin area. He decides that the expansion will be about 500 meters wide. How many kilometers is this?

NAME_____ DATE _____

They're Saying the Same Thing?
Moving between Measurement Systems

1. Franco Automobile Company is joining the growing trend of manufacturers and switching all of their measurements to the metric system.

   a. The table lists some of the measurements for items that the company has in its inventory. Use common conversions to convert these measurements to metric measurements. Show your work. Round your answers to the nearest tenth, if necessary.

Dimension	Customary Measurement	Conversion	Metric Measurement
Engine size	0.65 gal		L
Fuel tank capacity	18.5 gal		L
Bore measurement	3.5 in.		cm
Length of car	189.2 in.		cm
Mass of car	3307 lb		kg
Oil tank capacity	4 qt		L
Amount of steel	1700 lb		kg

b. A sedan that the company builds has recommendations for maintenance of the car. The company recommends that the owner change the oil every 7500 miles. Under the metric system, after how many kilometers should the owner change the oil?

2. Harold is buying a new car.

a. He is a very tall man and prefers cars with a high ceiling for comfort. He is shopping for cars online and finds one that has 43.3 inches of headroom listed. Another car that he likes has 99.3 centimeters of headroom. Which car has more headroom?

NAME_____ DATE _____

b. He is concerned about the fuel tank capacity of the new car he wants to buy. He commutes a long distance to work every day and does not want to constantly be filling the tank. He finds 3 cars that he likes online. The Skyte has a fuel capacity of 19 gallons. The Madrid has a fuel capacity of 64.4 liters, and the Cougar has a fuel capacity of 63.6 quarts. Compare the fuel tank capacities of the cars using both gallons and liters. Order the cars from least to greatest fuel tank capacity.

	Skyte	Madrid	Cougar
Gallons			
Liters			

12

Lesson 12.4   Assignment

NAME_____ DATE _____

Is That Appropriate?
Choosing Appropriate Measures

Patricia is running a summer science camp. The camp is a hands-on camp designed to introduce kids to all types of science.

1. In the Outdoor Skills Unit, Patricia wants the campers to learn to cook with solar power, build emergency shelters, and gather rainwater. Using what you know, select the appropriate measurement used in each activity.

   a. The rectangular solar panel used for cooking is 12 centimeters by 7 centimeters. Choose the best measurement to describe the area of the solar panel: 84 cm, 84 cm^3, or 84 cm^2. Explain your answer.

   b. Patricia has the kids gather sticks to make a rectangular roof for an emergency shelter. She wants the roof to be 8 feet long and 5 feet wide. Choose the best measurement to describe the perimeter of the roof: 26 ft, 26 ft^2, or 26 ft^3. Explain your answer.

   c. The campers must design a rainwater collection system. The tub that will collect the rainwater is a cylinder with a radius of 4 inches and a height of 12 inches. Choose the best measurement to describe the volume of the tub: 603.2 in.^{2}, 603.2 in., or 603.2 in.^{3}. Explain your answer.

   d. Patricia tells the campers that they need to dig a hole that has an approximate volume of 8 cubic yards that will be used to store cold items. What is one set of dimensions that could be used for the hole?

2. A group of campers at a summer science camp have to complete a physics unit. Before participating in the activities, their camp leader has them fill out a chart to find the most appropriate customary unit and metric unit that can be used to measure specific items. Complete the chart for the campers.

Activity	Metric Unit	Customary Unit
Bungee trampoline – determining the height of the jumps		
Archery – determining the distance of the arrow from the bulls eye		
Rocket launching – determining the height of the rockets		
Water displacement – determining the mass of large rocks		

3. A group of campers must navigate through the forest using compasses, topographic maps, and other devices. They must find 4 different locations. Using the clues below, determine how far it is from the start to each point on the map.

- The distance to point A is 1.5 kilometers.
- It is 0.5 more miles to get to point *B* from the start than to point *A*.
- The total distance to points A and D from the start is 3.1 miles.
- The distance from the start to point *C* is twice the distance from the start to point *B*.

a. How many kilometers is it from the start to each location?

NAME_____ DATE _____

b. How many miles is it from the start to each location?

4. A zip line activity is part of an obstacle course that a group of students must get through together. There are several zip lines on the course, the longest of which is about 72 meters long. How can this be stated using the most appropriate unit in the customary system? Show your work.

12

NAME_____ DATE _____

The Language of Geometry
Sketching, Drawing, Naming, and Sorting Basic Geometric Figures

1. List all of the different types of triangles you have learned about.

2. Can a triangle be both scalene and acute? Explain your reasoning and include a drawing to support your answer.

3. Can a triangle be both obtuse and isosceles? Explain your reasoning and include a drawing to support your answer.

13

4. Can a triangle be both right and obtuse? Explain your reasoning and include a drawing to support your answer.

5. Are all equilateral triangles acute? Explain your reasoning and include a drawing to support your answer.

13

NAME_____ DATE _____

6. List all of the different types of quadrilaterals you have learned about.

7. Are all squares rectangles? Explain your reasoning and include a drawing to support your answer.

8. Are all rhombi squares? Explain your reasoning and include a drawing to support your answer.

13

9. List the quadrilaterals that are parallelograms. Explain your reasoning and include a drawing to support your answer.

10. Is a kite a rhombus? Explain your reasoning and include a drawing to support your answer.

13

NAME_____ DATE _____

11. Are all trapezoids isosceles? Explain your reasoning and include a drawing to support your answer.

13

13

Lesson 13.2 Assignment

NAME_____ DATE _____

Weaving a Rug
Area and Perimeter of Rectangles and Squares

1. An artist is weaving a rectangular rug to match the pattern shown in the figure. Use the figure to answer parts (a) through (e).

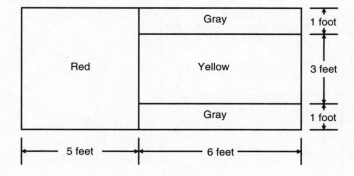

a. Calculate the area of the yellow region.

b. Calculate the area of the red region.

c. Calculate the total area of the gray regions.

d. Calculate the area of the entire rug. Show your calculation in two different ways.

e. Suppose that the artist wants to add a braid trim around the edges of the rug. How many feet of braid trim will the artist need?

2. Suppose you want to paint a rectangular mural. You want the perimeter of the mural to be 32 feet. Sketch three rectangles on the grid shown to represent three possible sizes for your mural. Each square on the grid represents a square that is one foot long and one foot wide. Which of the three murals has the greatest area? Which of the three murals has the least area? Show your work.

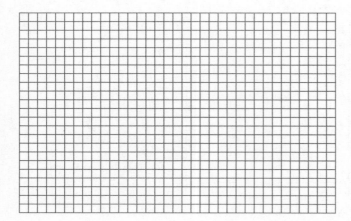

NAME_____ DATE _____

a. One tube of paint will cover 2.4 square feet. Calculate the number of tubes of paint needed for a mural the size of each of the rectangles you drew. Show your work.

b. One tube of paint costs $8.27. Calculate the cost of painting a mural the size of each of the rectangles you drew.

13

c. What size mural would you choose to paint? Explain your reasoning.

d. Your friend suggests that it would look nice if you framed the mural. Framing costs $2.89 per foot. Would adding a frame change your mind about the size of mural you paint? Explain your reasoning.

Lesson 13.3 Assignment

NAME_____ DATE _____

Boundary Lines
Area of Parallelograms and Triangles

1. An artist receives a request from a client to create a rug that is the shape of a parallelogram. The artist charges $25 per square foot of rug. The client decides to pay $600 for the rug. Draw two different designs for the rug on the grid. What is the area, base, and height of each rug? Show your work.

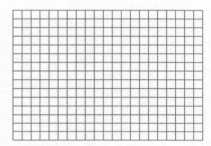

2. You are making a kite out of nylon fabric. The height of the kite will be 36 inches and the widest part of the kite will be 24 inches as shown in the diagram. How much nylon fabric will you need to make the kite? Write the answer in square inches and square feet.

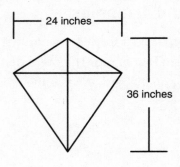

3. Figure *WXYZ* is a parallelogram and Figure *PXY* is a triangle.

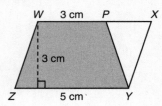

NAME_____ DATE _____

   a. Describe what strategy you could use to calculate the area of the shaded region.

   b. Use the strategy you described in part (a) to calculate the area of the shaded region. Show your work.

NAME_____ DATE _____

The Keystone Effect
Area of Trapezoids

1. A parallelogram, triangle, and trapezoid are shown.

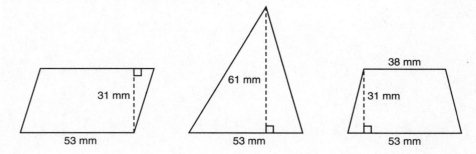

a. Without calculating the area, predict which figure will have the greatest area. Explain your reasoning.

b. Calculate the area of each figure and write it in the center of the figure. Show your work.

13

   c. Was your prediction in part (a) correct? Explain your reasoning.

2. A triangle, rectangle, and trapezoid each have an area of 24 square centimeters. Each figure also has a base of 6 centimeters.

   a. Make a sketch of the triangle, rectangle, and trapezoid as described above. Label the sketches with the given measures.

   b. Which figure do you predict will have the greatest height? Explain your reasoning.

   c. Write the formulas for calculating the area of a triangle, a rectangle, and a trapezoid.

NAME_____ DATE _____

d. Calculate the height of the triangle and write it on the sketch you made in part (a).
Show your work.

e. Calculate the height of the rectangle and write it on the sketch you made in part (a).
Show your work.

f. Calculate the height of the trapezoid, if the other base is 10 centimeters long. Write the height
and length of the second base on the sketch you made in part (a). Show your work.

g. Was your prediction in part (b) correct? Explain your reasoning.

13

Lesson 13.5   Assignment

NAME_____ **DATE**_____

Go Fly a Kite!
Area of Rhombi and Kites

Use quadrilateral *QUAD* to answer the questions.

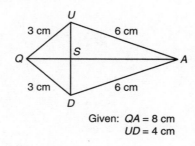

Given: *QA* = 8 cm
        UD = 4 cm

1. What kind of quadrilateral is *QUAD*? Explain your reasoning.

   a. Calculate the area of *QUAD*. Show your work.

   b. Cut out this copy of *QUAD*. (HINT: Before cutting out the kite, write the names of vertices inside the figure.) Then, cut kite *QUAD* apart along diagonal *QA*.

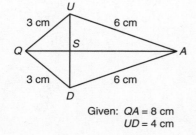

Given: *QA* = 8 cm
        UD = 4 cm

13

NAME_____ DATE _____

c. Rearrange the triangles formed from cutting apart *QUAD* so that they form a parallelogram. Tape the new parallelogram below.

d. Write the formula for the area of a parallelogram. Write the measurements of the base and height of the parallelogram on the figure in part (c), then calculate the area of the parallelogram. Show your work.

e. How does the area of the parallelogram in part (d) compare to the area of kite *QUAD*?

13

f. How does the base of the parallelogram relate to kite *QUAD*? How does the height of the parallelogram relate to kite *QUAD*?

g. Can you calculate the area of a kite by using only the lengths of the diagonals? Explain your reasoning.

NAME_____ DATE _____

Street Signs
Area of Regular Polygons

Quinnie wants to make a quilt using the Grandmother's Flower Garden pattern. This pattern requires assembling regular hexagons to form "flowers."

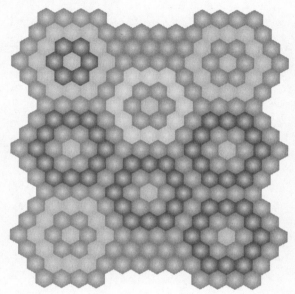

1. Quinnie wants the quilt to be at least 24 square feet (or 3456 square inches) so that she can put it on her single bed which is 39 inches by 75 inches. The pattern she plans to use requires that she cut out 228 congruent regular hexagons. She is trying to decide how big each hexagon should be. She has narrowed it down to the sizes shown.

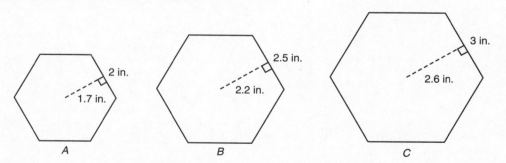

A   2 in.   1.7 in.

B   2.5 in.   2.2 in.

C   3 in.   2.6 in.

a. Calculate the area of Quinnie's rectangular bed. Show your work.

b. Which hexagon size do you predict Quinnie will choose? Explain your reasoning.

c. Calculate the area of hexagons A, B, and C. Show your work.

NAME_____ **DATE** _____

    d. Calculate the area that 228 size *A*, size *B*, and size *C* would each cover. Show your work.

    e. Which size hexagon should Quinnie use? Explain your reasoning.

Lesson 14.1   Assignment

NAME_____ DATE _____

Cut, Fold, and Voila!
Nets

1. In geometry, there are a group of solids known as the Platonic solids. Platonic solids are special because all of the faces on each solid are congruent. In addition to that, all of the sides and all of the angles on each face are congruent. There are five Platonic solids.

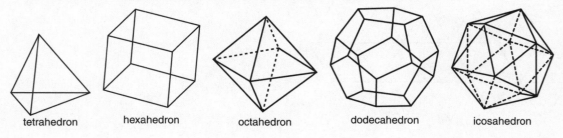

tetrahedron   hexahedron   octahedron   dodecahedron   icosahedron

   a. State the number of faces each solid has.

   b. What is the relationship between the name of the solid and the number of faces?
      (HINT: An octagon has 8 sides.)

14

c. Label each net with the name of the Platonic solid it forms.

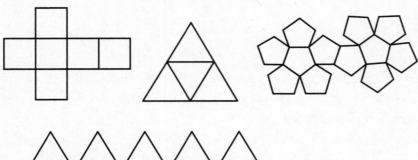

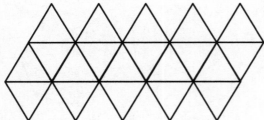

d. Consider the octahedron. Sketch each face of the octahedron and label the location of the face.

e. What do you notice about the faces of the octahedron that you sketched in part (d)?

14

NAME_____ DATE _____

    f. Draw a net for the octahedron.

    g. Draw a net for the octahedron that is different from the one you drew in part (f).

14

14

NAME_____ DATE _____

More Cans in a Cube
The Cube

In 1974, Erno Rubik created the very first Magic Cube, which later became known as the Rubik's Cube. Each face of the Rubik's Cube is a different color – red, orange, yellow, green, blue, or white – and each face is made up of nine smaller cubes. The Rubik's Cube is composed entirely of these smaller cubes, which are called cubelets. A drawing of a Rubik's Cube is shown.

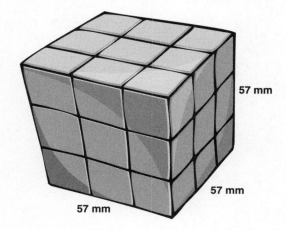

57 mm

57 mm

57 mm

1. Use the drawing of the Rubik's cube to answer the questions.

   a. Color the faces that you can see in the drawing. Color one of the faces red, one of the faces yellow, and one of the faces green.

14

b. Sketch and color each of the three remaining faces (those that you cannot see).

c. Use the dimensions given in the drawing of the cube to determine the length, width, and height of one of the smaller cubes, or cubelets. Explain how you determined your answer.

d. Calculate the surface area of the Rubik's Cube shown in the drawing. Show your work.

NAME_____ DATE _____

2. Use the drawing of the Rubik's cube to answer the questions.

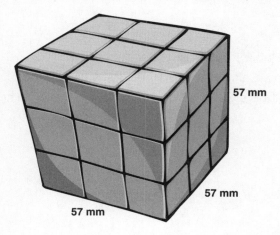

57 mm

57 mm

57 mm

a. Calculate the volume of one of the cubelets using the volume formula. Show your work.

b. Calculate the volume of the Rubik's Cube using your answer to part (a). Explain how you determined your answer.

c. Calculate the volume of the Rubik's Cube using the volume formula. Show your work.

14

d. Compare your answers to parts (b) and (c).

e. Suppose that you decide to make a model of a Rubik's Cube out of paper in which the dimensions are double that of a real Rubik's Cube. Calculate the volume of the larger model. How does it compare to the volume of the real Rubik's Cube? Show your work and explain how you determined your answer.

14

Lesson 14.3 Assignment

NAME_____ DATE _____

Prisms Can Improve Your Vision!
Prisms

1. Sketch an example of a prism you learned about in this lesson.

   a. Describe the number of faces the prism has.

   b. Describe the number of lateral faces the prism has.

   c. Describe the number of vertices the prism has.

   d. Describe the number of edges the prism has.

   e. Describe the shape of the base of the prism and name the prism.

14

2. Use what you know about prisms to answer the following questions.

   a. What is the relationship between the number of edges of the base and the number of vertices of the prism?

   b. What is the relationship between the number of edges of the base and the total number of edges of the prism?

   c. What is the relationship between the number of edges of the base and the number of faces of the prism?

NAME_____ DATE _____

Outside and Inside a Prism
Surface Area and Volume of a Prism

Khaled works for the Happy Camper tent-making company. He is working on a design for a new tent. A sketch of his design is shown. The tent is a right prism.

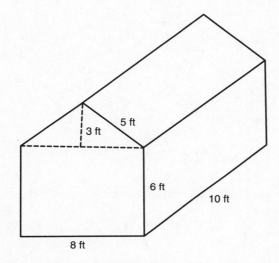

1. Use the sketch of Khaled's tent to answer the questions.

   a. What name best describes the shape of the bases of Khaled's tent design?

   b. How many faces of the tent design are lateral faces?

   c. What name best describes the shape of Khaled's tent?

14

d. Sketch a net and label the measurements for Khaled's tent design. Write the appropriate name on each face: front, back, right top, left top, bottom, right side, and left side.

e. Calculate the area of one of the bases of Khaled's tent using the measurements given in the sketch. Show your work.

NAME_____ **DATE** _____

    f. Are all of the lateral faces the same size? Explain your reasoning.

    g. Calculate the area of the lateral faces of Khaled's tent using the measurements given in the sketch. Show your work.

    h. Use your answers to parts (e) and (g) to calculate the surface area of Khaled's tent. Then, calculate the volume of Khaled's tent using the measurements given in the sketch. Show your work.

14

Lesson 14.5   Assignment

NAME_____ **DATE** _____

The Egyptians Were on to Something—or Was It the Mayans?
Pyramids

1. In 1984, the president of France commissioned architect I.M. Pei to design the Louvre Pyramid to be constructed in the main courtyard of the Louvre Palace in Paris, France. The Louvre Pyramid is 20.6 meters tall and is made of glass and metal. The Louvre Pyramid was built as an entrance to the Louvre Museum to help accommodate the many people who visit the museum each day.

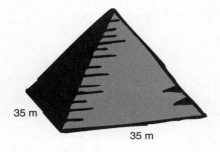

35 m

35 m

a. What is the best name for the shape of the Louvre Pyramid? Explain your reasoning.

b. How many lateral faces does the Louvre Pyramid have?

c. Identify the number of vertices, edges, and faces of the Louvre Pyramid.

14

d. Draw and label a net of the Louvre Pyramid.

e. The lateral surface area of the Louvre Pyramid is about 1890 square meters. The entire surface area of the Louvre Pyramid is about 3115 square meters. Does the lateral surface area or the entire surface area give you a better estimate of the amount of glass that was used to build the Louvre Pyramid? Explain your reasoning.

f. Using the information you have been given, can you calculate the exact amount of glass used to build the Louvre Pyramid? Explain your reasoning.

NAME_____ **DATE** _____

2. Your mom has asked you to build the family's tent for the camping trip this weekend. The family tent that you are building will be a hexagonal pyramid when you are finished.

a. Describe what your family's tent will look like once you have built it.

b. How many lateral faces will your family's tent have?

c. Identify the number of vertices, edges, and faces of your family's tent.

d. Draw and label a net of your family's tent.

14

Lesson 14.6   Assignment

NAME_____ DATE _____

And the Winning Prototype Is . . .?
Identifying Geometric Solids in Everyday Occurrences

1. Mary Alice loves to burn scented candles in her room. She has collected a number of uniquely shaped candles. What name best describes the shape of each candle?

a.

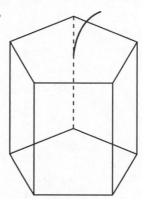

b.

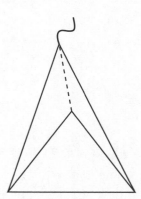

c.

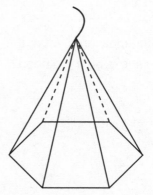

d.

14

e.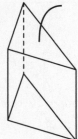

f.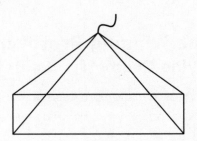

2. Mary Alice is going to give a candle to her best friend for her birthday.

   a. Mary Alice wants to give her best friend the candle that contains the most wax, so that it will burn for the longest amount of time. Does the measurement of surface area help her to determine which candle to choose?

   b. Mary Alice needs to purchase wrapping paper for this gift. Does the measurement of the surface area help her to determine the amount of wrapping paper she is going to need?

NAME_____ DATE _____

3. Mary Alice has decided to give her best friend a candle that has a surface area of 204 square inches. For $2.50, she buys a rectangular sheet of wrapping paper that is 24 inches by 19.5 inches. She plans to use this wrapping paper for the candle and other gifts that she plans to give.

   a. How many square inches are in one rectangular sheet of wrapping paper?

   b. Determine the cost of wrapping paper per square inch to the nearest hundredth of a cent. (Remember: When calculating an amount of money, always round up.)

   c. What was the cost of the wrapping paper required to wrap the candle Mary Alice will give as a gift?

Why Do We Use Statistics?
Designing Statistical Questions

1. The table shows the 10 most frequently occurring surnames from the 2000 Census.

Surname	Number of Occurrences
Smith	2,376,206
Johnson	1,857,160
Williams	1,534,042
Brown	1,380,145
Jones	1,362,755
Miller	1,127,803
Davis	1,072,335
Garcia	858,289
Rodriguez	804,240
Wilson	783,051

a. Were the surname data collected using a survey or an experiment? Explain your reasoning.

15

b. Determine the number of people in the 6th grade at your school that have one of the surnames listed in the table.

Surname	Number of Occurrences
Smith	
Johnson	
Williams	
Brown	
Jones	
Miller	
Davis	
Garcia	
Rodriguez	
Wilson	

c. Did you conduct a survey or an experiment to collect this data? Explain your reasoning.

d. What are the similarities between your data and the data from the census?

e. What are the differences between your data and the data from the census?

NAME_____ DATE _____

2. Tamara claims that Sweet Grove apple juice tastes better than Juicy Bushels apple juice. Isaac claims that there is no difference between the 2 types of apple juice. Tamara and Isaac would like to find the answer to the following question.

Do more 6th graders prefer Sweet Grove apple juice or Juicy Bushels apple juice?

a. Is this a statistical question? Explain your reasoning.

b. Can this question be answered with an experiment? Explain your reasoning.

15

Dealing with Data
Collecting, Displaying, and Analyzing Data

1. There are 533 verified skate parks in the United States. The table shows how many skate parks there are in each of the states listed.

State	Number of Skate Parks
Arizona	13
Colorado	26
Georgia	10
Massachusetts	14
Nevada	19
New Jersey	12
Tennessee	6
Washington	24

a. Is this categorical or quantitative data? Explain your reasoning.

b. Is this discrete or continuous data? Explain your reasoning.

15

c. Create a bar graph with horizontal bars using the data represented in the table.

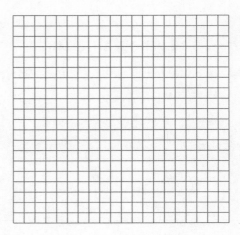

d. What do the bars represent?

e. Which state has the most skate parks? How many does it have?

f. Which state has the fewest skate parks? How many does it have?

NAME_____ DATE _____

2. The double bar graph shows the number of skaters who used Smooth Skate Park in one week. Use the double bar graph to answer the questions.

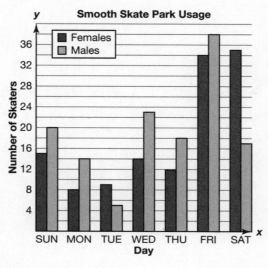

a. What does the key tell you?

b. What interval is used to record the number of skaters on the bar graph?

c. How many female skaters used the park during the week? Explain how you determined your answer.

d. What is the difference between the number of male skaters that used the park on Friday and the number of male skaters that used it on Saturday? Show your work.

15

e. On how many days were there more male skaters using the park than female skaters? Explain how you determined your answer.

f. Create a stacked bar graph using the data represented in the double bar graph.

g. The city would like to close the park one day a week for maintenance. Which day would you recommend they close the park based on the data shown in the bar graph? Explain your reasoning.

NAME_____ DATE _____

3. The city would like to know the ages of the skaters using Smooth Skate Park. They survey all of the skaters that use the park in one week. The results are shown in the circle graph.

Age of Skaters using Smooth Skate Park

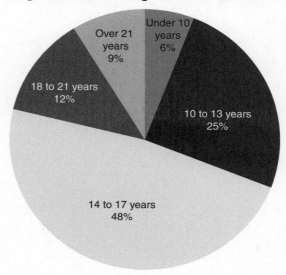

a. What percent of the skaters are under 10 years of age?

b. If 512 skaters were surveyed, how many skaters are 10 to 13 years old? Show your work.

Lesson 15.3 Assignment

NAME_____ DATE _____

At the Olympics
Line Plots and Stem-and-Leaf Plots

1. The table lists the ages of the players on the Atlanta Hawks basketball team for the 2010–2011 NBA season.

Player	Age
Joe Johnson	29
Jamal Crawford	30
Josh Smith	25
Al Horford	24
Marvin Williams	24
Mike Bibby	32
Maurice Evans	32
Zaza Pachulia	26
Jeff Teague	22
Damien Wilkins	31
Josh Powell	28
Etan Thomas	33
Jordan Crawford	23
Jason Collins	32

You are going to create a line plot to display the ages of the team members for the Atlanta Hawks.

a. Are the data in the table quantitative or categorical? Explain your reasoning.

b. What will be the title of your line plot?

c. What numbers will begin and end your number line? Explain how you chose those numbers.

d. What interval will you use on your line plot? Explain how you chose your interval.

e. Create a line plot displaying the ages of the team members for the Atlanta Hawks.

f. Examine the line plot you created for the ages of the team members for the Atlanta Hawks. Describe the distribution of the data in the line plot and any interesting patterns. Explain what your answer means in terms of the ages of the team members.

g. What do the 3 Xs above the 32 mean?

NAME_____ DATE _____

2. The table shows the number of wins and losses the Atlanta Hawks have had in 42 seasons. You will create a side-by-side stem-and-leaf plot of these wins and losses.

Season	Wins	Losses	Season	Wins	Losses
2009-10	53	29	1988-89	52	30
2008-09	47	35	1987-88	50	32
2007-08	37	45	1986-87	57	25
2006-07	30	52	1985-86	50	32
2005-06	26	56	1984-85	34	48
2004-05	13	69	1983-84	40	42
2003-04	28	54	1982-83	43	39
2002-03	35	47	1981-82	42	40
2001-02	33	49	1980-81	31	51
2000-01	25	57	1979-80	50	32
1999-00	28	54	1978-79	46	36
1998-99	31	19	1977-78	41	41
1997-98	50	32	1976-77	31	51
1996-97	56	26	1975-76	29	53
1995-96	46	36	1974-75	31	51
1994-95	42	40	1973-74	35	47
1993-94	57	25	1972-73	46	36
1992-93	43	39	1971-72	36	46
1991-92	38	44	1970-71	36	46
1990-91	43	39	1969-70	48	34
1989-90	41	41	1968-69	48	34

a. What numbers will you choose for your stems? Explain your reasoning.

b. How many leaves will you have on each side? Explain your reasoning.

15

c. What key will you use?

d. Create a side-by-side stem-and-leaf plot.

e. Explain why a side-by-side stem-and-leaf plot is a good way to display this data.

f. What observations can you make from the side-by-side stem-and-leaf plot? Describe your observations in your own words. Use what you know about the distribution and patterns of graphical displays for the side-by-side stem-and-leaf plot.

Lesson 15.4 Assignment

NAME_____ DATE _____

Building Up
Using Histograms

1. Amusement parks, theme parks, water parks, and zoos have been the source of entertainment since the late 1500s when the amusement park, Bakken, was opened in Denmark. Currently, there are almost 600 of these attractions all over the United States. The table shows the total number of amusement parks, theme parks, water parks, and zoos in each state in the United States.

State	Number of Amusement Parks, Theme Parks, Water Parks, and Zoos	State	Number of Amusement Parks, Theme Parks, Water Parks, and Zoos
Alabama	14	Montana	4
Alaska	5	Nebraska	7
Arizona	11	Nevada	11
Arkansas	7	New Hampshire	7
California	66	New Jersey	27
Colorado	15	New Mexico	5
Connecticut	5	New York	21
Delaware	5	North Carolina	11
Florida	44	North Dakota	7
Georgia	11	Ohio	17
Hawaii	6	Oklahoma	11
Idaho	5	Oregon	6
Illinois	10	Pennsylvania	38
Indiana	15	Rhode Island	3
Iowa	8	South Carolina	17
Kansas	5	South Dakota	11
Kentucky	7	Tennessee	10
Louisiana	9	Texas	28
Maine	5	Utah	2
Maryland	10	Vermont	5
Massachusetts	7	Virginia	13
Michigan	11	Washington	9
Minnesota	10	West Virginia	4
Mississippi	4	Wisconsin	11
Missouri	10	Wyoming	2

a. What intervals will you use to group your data? Explain your reasoning.

b. Create a frequency table for the number of parks and zoos in the United States. Make sure to name your table.

c. Create a histogram of the data in the table. Make sure to name your histogram.

NAME_____ DATE _____

d. Use what you know about the distribution and patterns of a graphical display to describe what the histogram says about the number of amusement parks, theme parks, water parks, and zoos in the United States.

e. Can you use the histogram to determine how many states have only 4 amusement parks, theme parks, water parks, and zoos? Explain your reasoning.

15

f. Create a stem-and-leaf plot of the park and zoo data.

g. How is the stem-and-leaf plot similar to the histogram you created in part (c) in what it tells you about the data?

Lesson 15.5 Assignment

Analyze This!
Designing and Implementing an Experiment

In this Assignment, you will design an experiment and then collect and analyze the data.

1. Write a statistical question that you can find an answer to by conducting an experiment in your classroom.

    a. Conduct the experiment and record the results.

    b. Construct a line plot of the data. Be sure to include a title.

15

c. Construct a stem-and-leaf plot of the data. Be sure to include a key.

d. Construct a frequency table of the data.

e. Construct a histogram of the data. Be sure to include a title and labels for your axes.

f. Using what you know about distributions and patterns of graphical displays, what conclusions can you draw about your data?

g. Compare the graphs. Describe their differences and similarities.

h. Which type of graph do you think is the best graph for your data? Explain your reasoning.

Lesson 16.1   Assignment

NAME_____ DATE _____

In the Middle
Analyzing Data Using Measures of Center

1. The rate at which crickets chirp is affected by the temperature. In fact, you can estimate the outside temperature by counting cricket chirps. As a homework assignment, Mr. Ortega asks each of his students to count the number of chirps they hear in 15 seconds at 8:00 PM. The results are shown.

    36, 37, 41, 39, 35, 39, 35, 39, 42, 37, 40, 35, 36, 37, 42, 35, 37, 37, 38, 42, 41, 37, 41

    a. Determine the mode for the number of chirps heard in 15 seconds.

    b. What does the mode tell you about the number of chirps heard in 15 seconds?

    c. Determine the median number of chirps heard in 15 seconds.

    d. What does the median tell you about the number of chirps heard in 15 seconds?

    e. Calculate the mean number of chirps heard by the students in 15 seconds.

    f. What does the mean tell you about the number of chirps heard in 15 seconds?

2. An estimate of the temperature outside can be calculated by adding 37 to the number of cricket chirps you hear. Chelsea used only a sample of six calculated chirps to get the following estimates for the outside temperature.

76, 74, 74, 76, 73, 77

a. Determine the balance point on the number line shown to estimate the mean number of chirps. Then, describe the steps you took to determine the balance point.

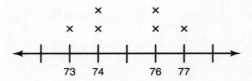

b. Calculate the mean from the data values. How does it compare to your answer from part (a)?

NAME_____ DATE _____

Which Measure of Center Should I Use?
Determining When to Use the Mean, Median, or Mode

1. The Branson Creek Middle School has decided to make fitness a key message to their students in the upcoming school year. As a result, they will be participating in a national fitness program. To participate, they must randomly select 15 students in the 5th grade and record their weights. The data (in pounds) are shown.

85, 80, 76, 78, 82, 88, 80, 80, 110, 85, 85, 82, 83, 88, 76

a. Construct a dot plot of the data on the graph shown.

b. Determine the mode for the weight of the students. Explain how you determined your answer.

c. What is the distribution of data? Do you think the mean weight is greater than, less than, or about the same as the median weight?

d. Explain how to calculate the median weight. Then, determine the median weight.

e. Determine the mean of the weights. Explain how you determined the mean.

16

f. Which measure of center, the mean or the median, would better represent the center of the data? Why?

2. Part of a national fitness program involves several daily activities for the students. One of the activities involves jump roping for 1 minute. The school must report the number of jumps per minute for a sample of students at the beginning of the year. The stem-and-leaf plot shown displays the number of jumps for the students in one fifth grade class.

Student	Number of Jumps per Minute
3	5 8
4	0 5 6 6
5	2 3 3 4 4 8 8
6	6 9 9 9
7	1 3 4

Key: 3|5 = 35 jumps

a. How many students are represented in the stem-and-leaf plot? Explain your reasoning.

b. What is the distribution of the data? Do you think the mean number of jumps is greater than, less than, or about the same as the median number of jumps?

c. Use a graphing calculator to determine the mean and median of the data set.

Lesson 16.3 Assignment

NAME_____ DATE _____

Picking a Player
Calculating and Interpreting the Mean Absolute Deviation

1. The Greenfield Company makes air conditioner units to sell to home construction companies. They get some of the parts for the air conditioner from another company. Unfortunately, this company is going out of business, so they must find a new source for the parts that they use. They narrow it down to two companies, Company A and Company B. They look at some samples for the number of days it takes each company to fill orders. The data is as follows:

Company A: 8, 6, 5, 9, 12, 15, 6, 9, 12, 8
Company B: 8, 10, 9, 8, 9, 8, 9, 10, 11, 8

a. Calculate the mean number of days it takes each company to fill the orders.

b. Based on the means, from which company should Greenfield choose to get their parts?

16

c. The dot plots of the data for each company are shown. Based on the dot plots, which company do you think has less variation in the number of days to fill an order?

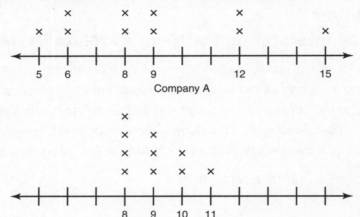

Company A

Company B

d. Complete the table to calculate the deviations from the mean of the number of days to fill the order for each company. Then determine the absolute deviation for each.

Company A			Company B		
Number of Days	Deviation from the Mean	Absolute Deviation	Number of Days	Deviation from the Mean	Absolute Deviation
8			8		
6			10		
5			9		
9			8		
12			9		
15			8		
6			9		
9			10		
12			11		
8			8		

NAME_____ DATE _____

   e. Calculate the mean absolute deviation for each company.

   f. What does the mean absolute deviation tell you about the number of days to fill the order for each company?

   g. Based on the results from part (f), which company should Greenfield choose?

2. A company has decided to run some tests on the assembly times of their air conditioners. They are concerned that the day shifts and evening shifts are not assembling the air conditioners with the same rates and consistency. The sample data they collect is as follows:

Day Shift (assembly time in hours): 2.5, 3, 2.75, 3, 3.25

Evening Shift (assembly time in hours): 3, 3.5, 4, 4.5, 5

a. Use a graphing calculator to calculate the mean and mean absolute deviation for each shift.

b. Based on your results from part (a), should the company be concerned?

Lesson 16.4 Assignment

NAME_____ DATE _____

Five Number Summary
Analyzing Data Using the Five Number Summary

1. The residents of Summersville, West Virginia, are concerned about people speeding through their town on US Route 19. The police decide to monitor the speed of the cars that pass through the town at various times during the day. The data show the recorded speeds in miles per hour of 23 cars at 7:30 AM on one Wednesday morning.

    73, 68, 72, 61, 51, 68, 70, 53, 72, 71, 46, 51, 55, 53, 65, 57, 65, 57, 58, 68, 61, 48, 83

   a. Construct a dot plot of the data. Describe the measure of variation of the data.

   b. Calculate the range of the data. Show your work.

16

c. Calculate the five number summary of the data. Show your work.

d. Interpret each number in the five number summary.

16

e. Calculate the IQR for the speeds of the cars. Show your work. What does the IQR value tell you about the speeds of the cars?

f. If the speed limit through the town is 50 miles per hour, do the residents have a right to be concerned based on this data?

g. Use a computer spreadsheet to verify the five number summary for the speeds of the drivers.

Lesson 16.5   Assignment

NAME_____   DATE _____

Box It Up!
Displaying and Analyzing Data Using Box-and-Whisker Plots

1. San Francisco, California, and Richmond, Virginia, are located at about the same latitude on opposite sides of the United States. The table shows the amount of rainfall each city gets on average each month.

	Jan.	Feb.	Mar.	Apr.	May	Jun.	Jul.	Aug.	Sept.	Oct.	Nov.	Dec.
San Francisco, CA	4.4 in.	3.3 in.	3.1 in.	1.4 in.	0.3 in.	0.1 in.	0.0 in.	0.1 in.	0.3 in.	1.3 in.	2.9 in.	3.1 in.
Richmond, VA	3.3 in.	3.3 in.	3.6 in.	3.0 in.	3.8 in.	3.6 in.	5.0 in.	4.4 in.	3.3 in.	3.5 in.	3.3 in.	3.3 in.

a. Calculate the range of rainfall in San Francisco. Show your work.

b. Calculate and interpret the five number summary for the rainfall in San Francisco.

c. Calculate and interpret the IQR for the rainfall in San Francisco. Show your work.

d. Calculate and interpret the range of rainfall in Richmond. Show your work.

e. Calculate and interpret the five number summary for the rainfall in Richmond. Then, calculate and interpret the IQR for the rainfall in Richmond. Show your work.

f. Construct box-and-whisker plots for the average rainfall for each city on the same graph.

16

g. Compare the rainfall in San Francisco and Richmond. Describe the shape of each box plot.

h. Do either of the cities have outliers? How do you know?